To: Blossom

Mercedes Jackson

ISBN 978-1-7368-8990-9

Published September 2021

To: Blossom

*This is for every little girl
who will one day be someone's hero.*

Blossom,

I want to start by saying that you don't need to have superpowers to be someone's hero. You'll understand that later in life.

When I found out I was pregnant, I was afraid of loving you. I was afraid of not being good enough for someone so pure and so beautiful—I was afraid of not being perfect. But the moment I looked into your golden eyes, I realized that everything happens as it should.

I loved you before I could even count your toes or place a million kisses on your button nose. I knew you were magical before the sparks escaped your fingertips. Your superpower isn't what makes you unique. Your greatest power is in the way you squint your eyes when the sun is setting in your window. It's in the loving way you cuddle up next to me when you aren't feeling well. It's your ability to pick me up when the weight of the world is on my shoulders. It's those curious hands and that large mind that make you blossom.

Your real superpower isn't something fantastical. It's the way you love, the way you dream, the way you hope and aspire. That adds to your creativeness, to who you are and what you'll become. All those things are what make you special. Your power is only found within, and you will discover this only when you love yourself completely.

As a growing young lady, I want you to surround yourself with people and things that nurture the soul. And remember to water your own garden. Don't seek validation from others, but try to find knowledge in everything. Remember, there is beauty everywhere, Love and happiness come from within. No mirror or photo will ever capture what's truly inside you. Guard your heart and be kind.

There will be secrets you'll have to keep and heartbreaks you'll have to endure. Just know that I'll be here every step of the way.

Forever and always,

Momma

1

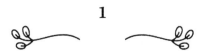

Growing up is already devastating. Imagine finding out that you'll gain superpowers when you hit puberty. Well, that's what happened to me. But before I entertain you and bore others, I guess it's only polite to introduce myself. Hello, I'm Blossom Nova, and I just turned nine a few months ago.

I'm named after the largest cherry blossom tree in Sibley Park. Momma says it's the most beautiful thing she's ever seen. And for some reason, it stays in bloom year-round. Momma and Daddy made it famous by getting married under it—at least, they looked like famous people in their wedding photos. And now it's become a tourist attraction in our little town.

In the picture on our living room wall, Momma's wearing a tiara and a long white gown with what looks like a million beads on it, made by some fancy designer whose name I can't pronounce. Momma sketched the dress, and Mr. Fancy Name created it. Then Granny Lily added the tiny beads, one by one, all by herself. The tiara shes's wearing has been passed down in the family for five generations. I don't know if the diamonds are real, but Momma keeps it locked in a safe in the attic. I'll be the next Nova to get it. But I don't like boys yet, so I don't know when that will happen. My favorite part of the picture is Momma's windblown veil. It's so long. Granny Lily says she spent three months making it.

In the picture, Daddy has on a light grey suit with a turquoise hanky in the pocket. Turquoise is one of my favorite colors. He was so handsome. I wish I could draw heart eyes on the photo, but Momma would kill me.

You see, I only got to know my daddy for one year. I don't remember anything about him besides his face, and that's only because I used to keep his picture under my pillow. But lately, I've been dreaming of him.

I still think Momma and Daddy used to be famous. There are pictures all over the internet of their wedding, of my birth, of Momma walking down the street, even of Daddy's funeral. Momma said she got a lot of attention because Mr. Fancy Name helped design her wedding gown. But I think it's really because she and Daddy were the most beautiful people in the world, and she's just being modest.

I like to read a lot, and I like to use words after I learn their meaning. The word *modest* pops up a lot in *The Modest King*, a book of Bible stories that my godmother Suri got me for Christmas last year.

Where was I? I am the perfect mix of my parents. I look a lot like Momma. People often mistake us for sisters, even when they've clearly heard me call her Momma. Besides, Momma is a grown woman and doesn't look like a kid. My dad and I have similar skin tones, and I have the exact same crescent-shaped dimple on my left cheek as he does—as he did.

I am almost five feet tall. That's pretty weird, considering I was only four feet, six inches last year. I could barely reach the kitchen faucet. I never thought I'd ever be able to see Momma over the kitchen counter. Now I can reach the Rice Krispie treats on the highest shelf in the pantry.

The more people say "Blossom, you're getting so big!" the more I want to find a magic potion that makes me stay a kid forever. It seems like life is butterflies and daisies for kids—at least that's what Granny Lily always says.

Believe me when I say I'm in no rush to grow up. I don't ever want to get too big to cuddle with Momma on movie nights or become a teenager and start drawing hearts all over my notebooks. I just want to play with my dollhouse and watch *Courage the Cowardly Dog* all day.

Poppy says I'm the smartest kid he knows, and I'm starting to think he's right. I've gotten 100s on my last ten spelling tests, and my teacher says that if I keep it up, she'll have to send me to college next year. It would be kind of cool to go from fourth grade straight to college, I guess. But I'm not ready to be a grown up yet, so I'll tell Mrs. Long that I'd prefer to just go to fifth grade like everyone else.

My favorite thing to do besides playing superhero with Momma is reading. We go to the bookstore every week. I can finish most books in two days, but Momma still only lets us go once a week. Next time, I'll just ask for two books. I wish we could go to another bookstore, though. The last time we went to 80 Percent Books on Seaside Drive, I picked up a copy of *Diary of a Wimpy Kid* and somehow got a splinter in my index finger. It stung, but we had to wait until we got home so Momma could use the tweezers to pull out the tiny piece of wood. I could hardly see it, but it hurt and bled really bad. Since then, I've been afraid to touch any of the shelves there. Anyway, I really only like that store because it's right next to the ice cream shop. Momma and I always order two double-fudge cones and read our books on the patio, with the waves of the ocean as our background music. I've read at least fifty books on that patio, which is a lot of double-fudge. Maybe next time I'll get rainbow sprinkles.

Wait a minute! There is something else I enjoy more than reading, and that's sleeping. My dreams are the coolest, especially because that's where I get to see my daddy. It wasn't until recently that I started having these dreams. But now Momma says I should start keeping a journal of them. I wish I could sleep forever, but Momma would miss me too much. Some nights, I feel her covering my cheeks in kisses, but my dreams keep me asleep, so I just try my hardest to smile to let her know I feel them.

At 10:30 in the morning last Saturday, it was 77 degrees outside, and Momma came in to put my laundry away as usual. The sun must have been playing hide-and-go-seek with my curtains, because as soon as she opened the door, a ray of light struck me in the face, turning the black space behind my eyelids where I see my dreams into a blood-orange splash of interruption. I jumped up abruptly, and I must've startled Momma because the next thing I knew, underwear and socks were flying all over. She screamed, I screamed—then we both erupted into laughter.

"Good morning, sunshine! Blossom, you must have slept right under the sun, because your hair looks like a field of wildflowers."

I guess that was a nice way of saying I had bedhead. I don't know what's been going on with my hair lately, but I can't seem to tame it. Poppy calls our hair the Nova curse. We all have these big heads of hair like no one else I've ever seen. I love it. Wearing my hair curly makes me feel powerful among all the girls at school who wear theirs straight or in braids. I love being unique. There are the nerds, the cool kids, and the rejects, and then there's me, Blossom.

Besides, flat irons are dangerous, with all the smoke and the ouches I hear my momma make. I'm a little too afraid to try.

After cleaning up the spilled laundry, Momma sat down on the edge of my bed. She kissed my forehead the way she always does, but this time it felt different.

From my earliest memories of Momma, we always shared an indescribable bond. Sometimes I can almost feel her thoughts through her kisses. It's weird, I know, but there's no other way to describe the surge that runs from my lips down and out through my toes. Granny Lily says it's because I love Momma so much, but I think it's magic.

"Momma, what's wrong?"

Momma looked sadder than usual. She tends to get a little depressed on the anniversary of Daddy leaving us to be with God. You see, my daddy died one day before my first birthday. I try not to mention him much around Momma, but it's hard to learn everything there is to know about someone you love if no one will talk about him.

Poppy says I started walking on my first birthday. He says it was God's way of putting me one step closer to my daddy. I hope he didn't mean that I was taking baby steps toward my own grave. But Poppy has a weird way of explaining things. I think he meant that God needed Daddy's help in heaven to guide me better on earth.

Granny Lily and Poppy are the only people who talk to me about Daddy, and that's only when we're alone. They tell me not to repeat anything to Momma. I don't blame them. We don't like to see Momma sad, and I'm sure the meteorologist on channel 9 wouldn't know how to explain what happens to the weather when Momma is sad.

2

"**B**lossom, we need to talk about something important."

"What is it, Momma?" I laid my head on Momma's lap so she could comb her fingers through my hair. I like it when she does that. It feels like her fingers are magically separating the gold, black, and honey-brown coils of my curls. I only like for her to touch my hair. It's like my hair has a powerful bond with Momma's fingers. My hair is a lock, and her hands are the secret code.

Poppy says there's power in my hair. Poppy also says he can lift cars with one finger, and no one can do that, but I still love his silly stories.

"Blossom, we need to talk about growing up."

"Momma, I know I'm going to grow up one day," I said with a giggle.

"Yes, but there's more to it than that. You are special, Blossom."

"I know, Momma."

"I mean, something is going to change within you, and you won't be able to control it."

Mrs. Long already told us that Mrs. Jo, the school nurse, would come talk to the girls about priority and something about periods when we get to fifth grade."

Momma laughed so hard you would have thought she was going to pee her pants, like I did when Sean the Stink Bomb farted and then fell out of his chair in the computer lab. "Baby, do you mean puberty?"

"Yes, Momma. I know about that stuff. I'm not ready, but I know it's going to happen one day." I giggled, knowing I don't feel happy about it inside. "But it's not going to happen until you stop calling me *baby*."

"You're right, Bab—Blossom. Well, what if I told you that on top of your body changing, you're going to get superpowers?"

"I'd say, duh! I already have superpowers! What else about my body will change?"

Momma must've seen a ghost, because her caramel-brown skin turned pale and her eyes went big like volleyballs. "What do you mean, you already have superpowers?" she stuttered.

"I'm super-smart. At least that's what you and Poppy and all my teachers tell me."

The copper tone of Momma's skin returned. She no longer looked like a Sweet Tart with the flavor licked off.

"I know what's going to happen. I have a billion years, though, Momma. I don't even have boobs yet." The word *boobs* makes me blush, but Momma lets me use it. She says all ladies have boobs, and we should embrace them, whatever that means.

"Blossom, you're going to go through a change. It happens to all of us. You're a kid one day, and then boom! an adult the next. You're going to grow breasts, and hair in places you're not used to seeing it. Your hips are going to get bigger. You'll gain weight. These little annoying bumps called pimples will show up from time to time, but thanks to your good Nova genes you shouldn't have to worry about those too much. But puberty brings other changes too."

"Like what? You mean there's even more than not being able to fit into my clothes, and bleeding every month, and turning into a cross between *Good Luck Charlie* and Phoebe from *The Thundermans*?"

Momma looked a little confused, but she nodded. "I guess, Blossom . . . well, eventually your toys and games will be less interesting. And, and . . ."

"Spit it out already! My stomach can't take this."

"One day, you'll find that you want to be more than friends with boys. Like hold their hand or go on dates with them."

My insides tightened. My mouth watered like it does right before I throw up. "Boys are so gross. They pick their noses and they don't brush their teeth, and I don't think any of them knows what lotion is. Besides, how could we go on a date? We're only nine and don't have any money. What, is Brandon's mom going to pick us up and take us to the movies, where we'll hold hands? Yuck!"

I don't think I said anything funny, but Mom was laughing. Probably a little too hard for this conversation. Or maybe she was crying hysterically.

"Oh, Blossom, I hope you stay this way forever! I know you're not ready for any of this. I just want to make sure you're aware of it, and that you feel comfortable talking to me about it."

"I do—I will. I already tell you everything."

"I know, B. Let's keep it that way."

In my mind, I was thinking maybe my hair would grow longer, or my clothes would get smaller. I wasn't at all prepared for the powers Momma explained would come with puberty.

"So, after puberty, I'll wake up one day and boom! I'm a grownup who wants to kiss boys?"

"Not exactly, but life will speed up a bit, or at least it'll feel that way. You'll discover later what I'm talking about. Don't think about it too hard."

I'd rather watch the rain splash against the window on hot summer days, or help a stranded ladybug conquer the jungle in our backyard. It makes me think back to the time when all I wanted was to be that spotted insect. Every time someone asked what I wanted to be when I grew up, I replied "A ladybug." There was always an uncertain pause, as they waited for me to say I was kidding, but I never said anything else. Who wouldn't want to be red with black speckles, being noticed by everyone while just being free?

After Poppy told me that being a ladybug is kind of silly, I settled on being a doctor. Not the kind who has to give shots or draw blood, because I hate those. Maybe I'll be a psychiatrist. I really love animals, too, but to be a veterinarian, I'll have to toughen up.

Momma told me that my allergies would need to clear up first. The allergist claimed I'd have to deal with the cough and itchy eyes for the rest of my life, like she was some sort of psychic.

I developed my allergies when I was three, after helping Poppy clean out the attic. Daddy's clothes and things were getting pretty dusty up there. Dr. Greystone tested me for allergies when I was six, after I'd made a lot of visits to the emergency room.

I remember that Momma would stay up all night with me, until I finally tired myself out from coughing. She never wanted me to feel bad for the sleepless nights. She says she got a lot of her best dress sketches from the lack of sleep.

We learned that I'm pretty much allergic to the outside world. Trees, grass, dogs, cats, perfume—life and everything I love. Ironically, I'm not allergic to any of the flowers that Poppy planted all over Anastasia. I rarely go to my friends' houses, because they all have dogs and there isn't enough Zyrtec in the world to stop me from sneezing a million times. It's embarrassing, especially my cough. Poppy says it makes me sound like an 80-year-old chain smoker.

All of these allergies mean that I'm not allowed to have any pets, except for the boring ones like fish and turtles. At this point, I'll take anything. It's lonely being an only child. Sometimes I get tired of hanging out with grownups, so I escape to my treehouse, to enter an imaginary world where I have lots of pets and siblings.

The only dog I can stand to be around for more than five seconds—or until they discover their tongue and lick my face—is my godmother Suri's dog. He's a black cocker spaniel named Othello, and he's *hypoallergenic,* which means I won't sneeze or cough after petting him. It took me forever to learn how to pronounce that word, let alone spell it. Momma still makes me take allergy medicine before I hang out with him, so I won't break out in hives.

Othello is cute and friendly, just a little needy, and he always tries to lick my face. If I become a veterinarian, the first thing I am inventing is a special pill to get rid of dog breath. Yuck! We hang out at Sibley Park. We run circles around the big cherry blossom tree, and the pink flowers always fall onto his shiny black coat.

My thoughts sometimes get carried away. Where was I? Oh yeah, Momma tells me that in just one year, my life will change forever.

If I stop telling Momma I need new underwear when they start getting tight, I wonder if it would prevent me from changing. But I think her naming me Blossom sealed my fate.

Who wants to grow up, anyway? If being a grownup is anything like the stories Poppy and Lily tell me on my weekend visits, then I'll pray every night to stay trapped in my nine-year-old body.

A few of the girls in my fourth-grade class are already starting to wear bras and like smelly boys. What could possibly be charming about Benny the Booger-Picker, or Charlie "The Skunk" Thomas?

Momma tells me that all boys have cooties, even the grown-up ones. I don't believe Daddy or Poppy has cooties, though. From the pictures in my baby album, Daddy was the most handsome man in the universe. His eyes were like burning embers. I guess that's where I got my hazel eyes from. His skin was shinier than a pot of gold. He was taller than any tree I've ever climbed, even the one Poppy built my treehouse in.

I dream of Daddy every night. My dreams seem so real—it's like he was never taken away. I don't understand why God allows some kids to have daddies and others to only have a mom, Poppy, and Granny Lily.

I like being a kid, and I'm going to do whatever it takes to stay one forever. That's why I play with my Barbies as much as I can, even though I'd rather play computer games. I wouldn't dare tell Momma that some toys bore me. She might cry, and sometimes when Momma cries, weird things happen. Granny Lily said that's why she and Poppy named Momma, Rain.

I was born on April 11, 1986. The saying that April showers bring May flowers came true that day. It rained from the time the sun came up until 11:58 p.m., when I was introduced to the world. Mom and Poppy thought of many names, but it just felt right to name their only daughter Rain. Poppy says that God himself named me.

My mom was in labor for almost 24 hours—she reminds me every time we disagree. Poppy says that on Mom's final push, I let out the loudest cry.

The newspapers from the day I was born mention a sudden, unexplained storm. It only lasted two minutes, but it shook the people living in Anastasia on the California coast. It was the worst storm the city had seen in years. The waves reached twenty feet high, lightning lit the entire sky, and rain fell at record rates—an estimated 9.5 inches in just those two minutes.

At midnight, the sky cleared like nothing had happened. And if that isn't weird enough, even without the sun shining hundreds of wildflowers started blooming all over the town.

Anastasia also wasn't ready for the bees that came with the flowers. When the news caught wind of the town's transformation, you would have thought the Great Wall of China had appeared overnight. Hundreds of reporters and tourists invaded our small town, which wasn't known for much other than its beauty.

The rolling green hills, and beautiful trees of Anastasia look like a painting. Every curve and crevice is a flawless creation from God. The ocean and streams are clear, the air is crisp, and it's always the perfect temperature. There aren't any huge buildings dominating the town like in the surrounding cities.

The people of Anastasia want to keep it as beautiful and pure as possible in a time of so much economic growth and so many pollutants. That's why so many people tend to walk or bike around town.

Houses are grand. Lawns are manicured. Life in the picture-perfect town is calm and quiet except for the rare bizarre feat of nature—rainstorms in cloudless skies causing beautiful, multicolored wildflowers to bloom all around. Especially in my parents' yard.

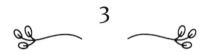

3

Poppy likes to tell me stories. Telling stories keeps him young. Momma says his stories are mostly make-believe, but something inside of me says there's some truth to them.

Poppy told me about the terrible storm that happened after my daddy died. I don't remember much. Or at least I shouldn't—I'm not sure how old I was, or if it was a dream, but in my little world there was once a bad storm that seemed like it would never end.

Poppy told me the worst part of the storm happened at Daddy's funeral. It rained so hard we had to run for shelter inside the cement building where the dead people are kept. I felt scared hearing this story. Poppy said the more Momma cried, the harder it rained. The sadder she got, the louder the thunder roared. Granny Lily tried her hardest to comfort Momma, but nothing would help. Granny said Momma's heart was broken, and she and Poppy weren't sure if it would ever heal. Daddy was the love of her life. I'm not too sure what that means, but if Momma loved him as much as she loves me, then I know she loved him a lot.

I even heard about the storm at school. No one could ever explain what happened that day. Especially since it's always sunny in Anastasia.

Momma is the strongest woman I know. I remember her working long hours right before she opened her own dress shop—studying late nights while still finding time to tuck me into bed; being there when I woke in the morning. I'm convinced she never sleeps. Well, except on Saturday nights when I make her watch the Disney Channel. Cartoons are like a lullaby for her.

After Daddy died, Momma left her job at *ACAL Magazine* to pursue a career in fashion design. These days, she doesn't pick up a pen much. I miss Momma reading me her magazine articles before bed. But she says that she wanted to design dresses for as long as she can remember.

For a little while after Daddy died, we struggled with money. Momma worked with Miska Ré for six months while she was attending fashion school at night, and Poppy and Granny Lily helped us out until she graduated.

Now Momma owns her own dress store, the Hidden Orchid, named after the treehouse Poppy built for her when she was a little girl. Granny Lily painted an orchid on the front door of the treehouse, and she painted the same one on the black shiny door of the Momma's store. She works long hours sometimes, but I get to hang out with her. I am so proud of her. She is my very own superhero.

Although I am getting older, I still make my way to Momma's bed some nights. Momma likes when

I cuddle with her. She doesn't like sleeping alone since Daddy's no longer around.

My dreams about Daddy are always happy. Every night, month, and year is a continuation of his life as if he'd never died, but with only the two of us. Momma, Poppy, and Granny Lily are never there, but we talk about them. I get to tell him about my day, and Daddy always kisses me. And before I wake up, he says "I love you forever and always."

Momma says that's just God's way of telling me that even though Daddy has left us physically, he'll be there forever to protect me.

The dream I had last night was different. It wasn't happy. I dreamt that I woke up to Daddy lying on the pillow next to me, stroking my cheek and running his fingers through my hair. He looked like something was wrong. I smiled like I always do and kissing him on the nose I said, "Good morning."

He said, "Good morning, sunshine." But there was sadness in his eyes.

"What's wrong, Daddy? Is my breath stinky?" He laughed with his eyes. Tiny creases appeared around them—that's how I know Daddy is going to laugh or smile.

"No, baby, your breath isn't stinky. But I need to talk to you about some things that are going to change."

I touched his face. "Momma told me."

"She did?" Daddy looked surprised. "Well, don't be afraid. Daddy will be here to help you through it all. You're growing up to be a beautiful young lady, but just promise me you'll always remain Daddy's little girl."

"Forever and always, Daddy. Why does that make you sad? We all have to grow up."

"I know, sunshine, but you're a lot more special than most little girls."

"Duh!" I laughed at daddy telling me something I already knew. Everyone on earth is special in their own way.

"You're a Nova, Blossom. After this year, nothing about you will never be the same. And it's going to start with your beautiful curls."

"Daddy, I think you need to go back to bed. My hair is the least of our worries. I'll just start brushing it more." I kissed him on the forehead and patted his face. Then we put our heads together, and he touched the crescent shaped dimple on my left cheek, and I woke up.

Sparks from the purple and blue candles fell onto my Oreo ice-cream cake. I took the deepest breath I could and exhaled all the air from my nine-year-old lungs—and *poof!* I'm ten.

Last night I dreamt that Blossom started her period. I've never been happier to wake up. I don't know how long dreams last, but this one seemed like just three minutes or so. Blossom looked a lot younger, too—maybe five or six. She walked in with a bulge in the front of her favorite pink polka-dot tights.

"Blossom, what's wrong with your pants?"

"I put tissue inside my panties, because when I went to go pee there was a red spot."

I asked her to pull them down to show me, and found a huge red bloodstain. I gasped, and told her to pull up her pants, and then the dream was over.

With a foggy mind and a crook in my neck, I rolled over and called my parents' house. It was their weekend to keep Blossom, but I needed to speak with her now.

After the phone rang for what seemed like hours, Poppy answered in a groggy but alarmed voice.

I didn't even say hello. All I could do was blurt out, "Where's Blossom?"

"Rain, do you have any idea what time it is? Are you OK?"

Looking at the flower clock on my nightstand, I saw that it was 5:45 a.m. "I'm OK, Poppy. Please put Mom on the phone."

My mom is a light sleeper. After she took the phone from Poppy, she asked if I'd had the dream again.

"The one where my baby grows up?"

"Yes, Rain."

My powers don't make me clairvoyant, so I'm not sure how to process my dreams. Maybe my subconscious is letting me down easy, or maybe the unwanted but expected menstrual cycle will arrive sooner rather than later. If it arrives before she gets her powers under control, dangerous things could happen. I didn't start my own period until I was eleven, so I've been hoping that I have at least another year before Blossom takes the big leap over the young lady pond.

At Blossom's age, I never wanted to call it my period. So, Mom and I decided on the more discreet word *ruby*. Anytime I was in a bad mood, my parents would say, "A jewel thief must've taken our precious baby and replaced her with this ruby."

As I got older, I came to appreciate the word more. *Period* just sounds so final and blah. *Ruby* is much more powerful, like a rare red stone. A woman's menstrual cycle is powerful and precious and shouldn't be thought of as something negative. Girls are often stigmatized and teased, and I want Blossom to embrace her femininity and the changes in and of her body. I don't want her to be afraid or embarrassed when it happens at school but to feel empowered and recognize that she's growing into a strong young woman.

4

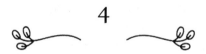

After spending most of the summer with my grandparents, I'm so ready to go back home before starting fifth grade. I just learned that I have to wear glasses. Momma and I picked out some cool, thick-framed, black and red Ray-Bans. They should be ready by next week. Hopefully I won't get teased for needing help to see. If only I could use my future powers to correct my vision.

As I ran down the stairs to see if my pizza rolls were done baking, I overheard Granny Lily talking to Mom. Granny always talks on speakerphone, even when the call is supposed to be private.

"Rain, I think we need to get Blossom bigger bras. I noticed hers are getting snug."

"OK, Mom," my momma sighed. "What am I to do with this girl? Have you noticed any powers?"

"No, not yet."

I couldn't take any more talk about those stupid bumps on my chest, so I walked into the kitchen hoping to stop it. I asked what time lunch would be ready, just to put me out of my misery, but Granny Lily just shooed me away.

Taking a seat by the window, I saw Poppy outside pulling weeds, so I jumped back up and told Granny Lily that he looked thirsty, and she should take him some water. Poppy had stopped letting me fix his water after I dropped a few ice cubes on the floor and forgot to rinse them off. When I gave him his favorite glass jar, there was dirt floating to the top.

"Honey, I have to go. Your dad needs some water."

"OK. I love you, Mom."

Before Granny Lily could hang up, I asked what they'd been talking about, even though I had heard everything. I hated any talk of boobs, especially mine.

"Your mom just wanted to check up on you. She'll pick you up this evening."

"OK, Granny. I'll pack after lunch."

"That's Granny's baby." She winked at me. Something about her reaction made me wonder if she knew I was eavesdropping.

After saying my prayers, I closed my eyes and drifted off into the place where I meet Daddy. I started having these dreams two years ago. I used to dream about school, vacations with my grandparents, or eating ice cream on the marina. Now I just have conversations with Daddy. I didn't realize you could miss a stranger so much until I dreamt about him.

The first dream scared the living daylights out of me. I recognized Daddy's face from all our pictures, but in my dream, he had aged a little more and seemed to know everything that was going on in my life, like he'd never left. The dream was so real that I slept in Momma's bed for a week, but I slept badly and stopped dreaming of Daddy altogether, so I moved back into my own room, and just like that he reappeared. He said that he missed me, and that he can only visit when I'm asleep in my own room. Since I have my own room at Granny Lily and Poppy's, he can visit me there too.

I always touch his face. I also hold my hand up to his chest so I can feel his heartbeat. I know dreams aren't real, but I don't ever want to forget him.

Momma likes to hear every detail when I wake up. She keeps a journal by her bed to keep track of my dreams. There are more than ten full journals now, on the bookshelf in my treehouse. One time, when Daddy visited my dream, he took one down, but when he turned the pages, they were all blank. Momma's handwriting isn't great, so maybe the Dream Keeper prevented Daddy from reading the journals because it would take up too much of our time together.

Momma thinks my dreams are Daddy's way of letting us know that he never left. She never dreams of him, so I don't mind sharing my dreams. I know she misses him too. She asks a lot of questions and always wants detailed replies. "What was he wearing?" "How did he smell?" "Is he happy?" Blah, blah, blah—then tears.

Last night's dream was a little different. Instead of only talking, Daddy gave me a gift too. Nothing I wanted, though—it was weird. He seemed sad and handed me a small silver box. I thought I was getting earrings, but there were two small flowers inside. Daddy called them rose buds. Then he kissed me on the forehead. I remember feeling the wetness of his tears on my face, but before I could ask about them the sun came into my room and turned the backs of my eyelids orange. Just like that, I was awake.

5

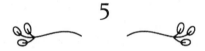

The palm of my hand ached from clenching the silver box. But when I opened it, there was no box. There were just two rosebuds.

Momma had picked up my glasses before bringing me home from my grandparents. I grabbed the plastic frames from the nightstand and put them on my face. I know I'm just supposed to wear them to see things that are far away, but maybe my vision was getting worse if I was imagining things in my hand. I blinked to help my eyes adjust to my new glasses and opened my hand again. The rosebuds were still there.

I flung my new blue comforter aside and ran to the door, almost tripping over my laptop that I'd forgotten to put back on the desk. I'm glad Momma didn't wake up before me, or she would've given me a lecture about not taking care of my things and blah, blah—yell. I ran to her room.

"Momma," I whispered, shaking her gently.

Momma doesn't sleep hard, so she opened her eyes right away. "Good morning, baby. Are you OK?"

"Yes, Momma. I had a dream about Daddy."

She pushed herself up by the palms of her hands and propped her pillows against the headboard so she could sit comfortably. Then, taking her glasses and journal from the purple nightstand in one motion, she was ready to document my dream.

"Momma, this dream wasn't like the others. Daddy was so sad." I was speaking so fast that Momma motioned for me to stop so she could write it all down. Instead I opened my hand, showing her the now-crushed rosebuds.

"What are those, Blossom?"

"Daddy gave them to me."

Momma's mouth fell open, but no words came out.

"He just handed them to me and said, you're growing up. Then he kissed my forehead, and he was crying."

"I have to call Poppy. Go to your room, and don't come out until I come to get you."

I went back to my room nervously. Momma had taken the rosebuds out of my hand. I hoped she would give them back. I wondered, if I ask Daddy for a new iPhone tonight, could I get it in my dream by next week? Then Suri wouldn't have to wait until my birthday to buy it for me.

Momma took forever to get off the phone, so I decided to pick out my clothes for school. Granny Lily liked to buy me clothes, so my closet was packed. Momma had organized it by color and type of clothing to make it easier to put away the laundry, and to stop me from only wearing my three favorite outfits over and over.

I took out some denim Bermuda shorts and a purple tank top that read *I AM NOT A MORNING PERSON*. I didn't want to go downstairs just yet, so I grabbed my favorite stuffed pink poodle, Tiff, out of the toy bin and started running my fingers though her yarn coat. Tiff is cute. I hope I get over my annoying allergies so that I can get a real puppy for Christmas.

As I sat down on my unmade bed, a blue jay landed on the windowsill. I didn't think anything of it, since I sometimes throw old bread or food scraps out the window. Especially vegetables. They're disgusting. But I hadn't seen a blue jay here before, and I remembered from one of Poppy's nature magazines that they live in the northeastern and southern states, not in the west. But I shrugged and continued to pet Tiff on the head, till I heard tapping on the glass.

Just then, Momma called my name from downstairs. She shouted to get ready because we would be leaving soon.

I grabbed my silver sandals from the shoe bin. I'm running low on summer shoes; my feet are getting so big. I'm down to three pairs of sandals. I saw some cool brown ones at the mall last week, with a purple string that wrapped around the ankle, and I hoped that was where we were going. I'm long overdue for new clothes too. I don't know why Momma doesn't just make my clothes. But I guess she designs dresses, and I'd rather not wear one every day. I'll stick to the mall.

The tapping repeated, and I looked to see the jay knocking on the glass with its beak, as if it was trying to get my attention. Hesitant, I walked to the window. I was careful to open it without scaring the bird—or myself. The little jay hopped to the left, moving out of the way, but didn't fly off. Something must be wrong. But it hopped back to where it was, perfectly fine.

Then it opened its beak and said, "I need your help!"

I jumped back, dropping my sandals to the floor. I was about to run, but I stopped and reasoned with myself. There's no way that bird just spoke—right? I slapped my forehead. Why am I even asking that?

As I walked back to the window, this time to close it, the pretty blue bird opened its beak again. "Blossom, my name is Jewel. I know you're thinking about a lot right now. We'll discuss it later, but right now I need your help. My husband Theo is hurt. He's on the doorstep of your treehouse." The jay lifted a wing, motioning in the direction of the treehouse.

My mouth went dry. Its voice wasn't screechy, like a parrot or like talking birds in movies. It was a normal voice with a Caribbean accent. Not what you'd imagine from a non-tropical bird. I gulped, hoping to create some moisture so I could swallow, but it didn't work. I guess that's what fear feels like.

"Follow me!" Jewel took flight.

I shook my head, hoping everything would return to normal, but it didn't. I quickly gathered myself. I would have to help this bird and figure out why it could talk to me later.

Before I could turn the knob of my closet door to go to my treehouse, I ran into Momma, and we both fell backward on the floor.

"Slow down, honey!" She helped me stand back up.

"Sorry, Momma, but I have to go!"

"I know you do. I've been calling your name. We need to go to your grandparents—"

Before she could finish, I said "I think I have a superpower."

Momma's eyes opened wide. I noticed that they looked lighter than normal. She hesitated and finally got out the words "Show me."

"I'm not really sure how it works yet. Just follow me."

She looked confused, but she stayed right behind me as I opened the door to my treehouse. It creaked a little. It had been a while since I used this entrance.

On the purple rug were two blue jays. They looked identical, except one is lying down, which I assume is Theo. I got down on my knees.

"Be careful, Blossom."

"What's wrong?"

Jewel told me how they had been migrating but were separated from their flock when she had to rest. Jewel is pregnant with their first hatchling. As they were resting in a tree in the park, the branch broke. Theo didn't react in time, and he hurt his right talon.

"How did you get into my treehouse? Why did you come to me?"

"Let's say the wind brought us here. There hasn't been someone like you in more than 300 hundred years. Blossom, you are an animal healer."

I fell back on my butt. "Momma, did you hear that?"

Momma was looking patiently at me. "I just heard you and a bunch of chirping. I guess you can understand birds?"

"Yes. This is Jewel and Theo. Jewel told me that I can not only talk to animals, I can heal them too." I turned back to Jewel, curious. "Can I understand all animals?" My heart raced with excitement.

"No—just those who need your help. The sick and weak, the injured."

This news made me a little sad. It would be cool to be able to talk to all animals. Like Dr. Dolittle. But it felt good knowing that I could help animals. And it would be amazing when I went to college. I wouldn't have to study or even know what tools or medicines to use. I could just use a magic wand or something. I could feel my own mouth still hanging wide open. And that dry feeling in my throat came back. I turned to look at Momma again.

Tears were forming in Momma's eyes. I don't know if she was scared, sad, amazed or all of the above. I am definitely scared, and a little confused, but I am excited to learn about my power, and that I could help animals.

Jewel cleared her throat, interrupting our moment.

"I'm sorry. How exactly do I heal Theo?"

"That's why we're here."

I thought back on every movie I'd seen about magic. But I didn't have a wand or a potion. Not even a fairy godmother. I closed my eyes, took a deep breath, and held out a shaking hand to carefully pick up

Theo's mangled talon. I imagined myself operating on the injured bird, like I had seen a thousand times on the Animal Channel.

"Blossom, open your eyes," Momma whispered.

Opening one eye at a time, I saw little gold sparkles dancing around Theo. In the corner of my eye, I saw Jewel jumping up and down. Theo, no longer in shock, opened his eyes. He shook his head the way I had just done in my room. He was probably just as confused.

"Thank you, thank you!" Jewel flew up to my face, her beak hitting my cheek. I guess this is a bird's way of kissing. A little groggy, Theo managed to say thank you as well.

"You have a special gift, Blossom. We hope to visit you again next year."

Still confused, I shook my head yes. Then I opened the door, wished the two blue jays well on their journey, and closed it after they flew off.

I turned to face Momma. She was pinching her arm, like she always does to stop from crying.

"This is great, Blossom! But you must be very careful with your power. You can't use it at school, or in the presence of anyone outside of our family. Promise me."

"Not even Suri or Mrs. Joy?"

"No one." Momma's face was serious. The water that had been trying to escape from her eyes was no longer there.

"I promise. But how do I control my power?"

"Do you remember me mentioning the *Nova Book of Magic*, that hasn't been seen in years?"

"Yes."

"Well, I've had it for years. I buried it under the cherry blossom tree in Sibley Park after your daddy died. I blamed our family's magic for his death. I read that book over and over searching for answers— for a way to bring him back. And when I realized I couldn't, I thought that hiding it might save you from getting a power. That didn't work either. The book explains how to control your power. We have to go dig it up."

This was way too much for me to take in all at once. I just stood there, speechless, feeling the dryness take over my throat again.

"I need water." Those were the only words that made sense to say.

Momma grabbed my hand and we ran out of my treehouse and back through the closet. In the kitchen, she grabbed her keys and a bottle of water from the counter, and then we ran to the garage and climbed into the SUV. Before buckling my seatbelt, I thought we might need shovels, so I hopped back out and grabbed the two shovels from behind the black trashcan in the corner. I tossed them in the back as I jumped into my seat. Then Momma reversed out of the garage so fast that we almost hit the mailbox. Sibley Park wasn't far. I smiled as we drove through the neighborhood. When we passed my school, I felt a surge of excitement at the thought of all of the cool new clothes I would wear. Then I felt a nervous pinch in the pit of my stomach. At that moment, I knew my days of being a little girl were coming to an end. So that I wouldn't start crying in the backseat and make Momma cry too, I pinched myself. Then I remembered that she'd said she had something to tell me before I blurted out about my power.

Momma pulled slowly into a parking spot by the lake. Before she put the car in park, I asked her what she and Poppy had been talking about.

"Oh yeah. Poppy told me that it's possible your dad is contacting you from heaven."

"Duh, Momma."

"No, Blossom, I mean it's really him, not just a dream."

A chill passed through my body. I felt the sensation flow through my fingertips and toes. I could see Momma's eyes in the rearview mirror, and she was crying. Overwhelmed with emotion, I started to cry too. Little drops of rain hit the windows of our SUV. Momma patted the seat next to her. That was her way of asking me to hop into the front.

I climbed forward, kissed Momma on the cheek, and wiped her tears with my fingers. Then before I could sit down, I felt a sudden shock. Momma must've felt it too because she pulled my hand away from her face. The rain stopped.

"Did you feel that?"

"Yes, did it hurt your heart?" Momma asked. She looked scared.

"No, Momma. I felt a shock, but it went through my hands and toes."

Laying her head back into the headrest, Momma covered her face with her hands and let out a low sigh.

"Is everything OK, Momma?"

"Yes, baby. That shock just confirmed that you're growing up. That's all."

"Do you have a power, Momma?"

"I do, but we'll save that for another day. Now let's grab those shovels and find the *Nova Book of Magic*."

Momma likes to end conversations when she's uncomfortable. I hope she tells me soon. I have a strange feeling that her power has something to do with the weather.

6

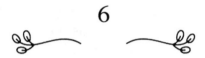

S chool wasn't as exciting as I expected. Seeing my friends was great, but holding on to this secret had my stomach in knots. Usually I sit in the front, but I picked a table in the corner this time. What if my power got out of control? Would the teacher call my mom, or send me to the nurse, or donate me to science? My throat was dry, my palms were sweating, and I could barely read Mrs. Cuso's name on the board—when I squinted my eyes, I thought it said Mrs. Queso.

I took my glasses out of the small pocket of my backpack and put them on. Emma was the first to notice. She also had a problem whispering, and she just shouted, "Your glasses are so cute!" across the room. I hunched down in my seat, hoping that all twenty-seven kids wouldn't look, but all twenty-eight—including Mrs. Cuso—turned to face me.

"You look so pretty, Blossom," one of the new kids said.

I whispered, "Thank you."

Most of us had grown up together, but with all the new businesses opening near Momma's dress store, more and more people had been moving to Anastasia recently. Another kid said he wished he wore glasses. Feeling more confident, I pushed myself back up in my seat.

"OK, kids, let's take a moment to introduce ourselves. I see a lot of new faces."

The rest of the day was a breeze. I hadn't gotten a chance to read the *Nova Book of Magic* yet, but thankfully I had no troubles with my new power. Just to be sure, Momma had stayed home from work and bought me a cell phone. She told me to text her if anything strange happened. I didn't have to text her at all until recess.

Emma, Jade, and I were sitting under the big jacaranda tree. It didn't provide much shade, but it was pretty—even though I would sometimes sneeze three or four times before my nose got used to the fragrance. The boys avoided the tree because they said it was too girly, which was great for us because boys are so annoying.

Under the tree, we caught up on what we'd done over the summer. The cool grass tickled my ankles as the breeze blew through my curls. I was careful not to mention my newfound power. Jade told us how excited she was to finally get boobs. I cringed. My own boobs brought on every feeling but happiness. It would be cool if she had a power too, but she didn't mention anything other than her excitement about wearing a bra.

Mrs. Cuso gave the five-minute hand signal that recess was almost over, and I decided to lie down in the grass for a bit. The sun was warm on my face, and my mind at peace, until I felt a sudden tug on my hair. My friends love playing with my hair, but this was different. Emma screamed.

"Blossom, move! There's a raccoon touching your hair!"

Oh no! My eyes were wide, but I didn't make any sudden moves. From the corner of my eye, I saw Jade and Emma running toward our teacher. This was my chance to talk to the raccoon.

"I know why you're here. Meet me at my treehouse after school. Go now, before the janitor gets you."

I didn't even get the raccoon's name. It nodded and dashed away just in time. When I rolled over, Mrs. Cuso, Jade, Emma, and the janitor were surrounding me. The janitor was holding a broom over his head. I'm not sure what he was planning to do with it.

"Are you OK, Blossom?"

"Yes, I'm fine."

"Were you scared?" Jade asked.

"Not at all. I just told the raccoon to go away, and that's what it did."

"I thought raccoons were nocturnal," Mrs. Cuso pondered, scratching her chin.

I shrugged and stood up to brush the grass off my new capris. "We should go inside. The bell is going to ring."

The fifth graders lined up to go back to class. While walking down the hall, I overheard Ashley telling Sarah that she saw me talking to the raccoon. My heart fell to my toes. When we got to our class, I asked Mrs. Cuso if I could go to the restroom. On the way out, I grabbed my phone to text my mom.

I didn't go bra shopping with my own mom until high school. Unlike my daughter, I always wanted to wear a bra. Mom even let me wear a light-blue terrycloth bikini top, with two strawberries to cover my unmentionables, to preschool. Unfortunately, I was a late bloomer.

Bra shopping is always devastating for Blossom and me. It seems like her breasts grow larger every month, and her granny and I have to buy her new bras to keep up several times a year.

"What are you feeding this child?" Mom laughed.

"Look, Granny!" Blossom started jumping up and down. "My new boobs shake when I move. Do yours do that?"

This time, we both fell over in laughter.

"Child, they used to. If I tried that now, these things would scrape the ground."

"Granny, you're silly."

"Mine didn't shake until after I bought them." We all laughed again.

We had an assortment of sports bras. She wasn't ready for actual cups. Blossom thought cups were too adult. We picked out bras in 34s, 36s, and 38s. Some of them had neon stripes, while others were solid, cool colors. Lace was forbidden, so we stuck to poly blends. She tried on all the bras, but the 38s fit the best.

It was an emotional bonding moment. I tried to hold back my tears, but they fell anyway.

"Mom, don't cry," Blossom whispered.

"I don't mean to, B. My baby is growing up." I started crying harder, to the point of sniffling.

"It's happening, whether we like it or not. I'm still a kid—just now I have boobs."

"You're so mature about this."

"Besides, boobs are the weirdest part of the body. They're just large lumps of fat."

"You're right, honey. Get dressed so we can get out of here. Hopefully it didn't rain too hard while we were inside." I winked at Blossom. We walked out of the fitting room and to the cash register hand in hand.

The car ride home was quiet. I turned on my iPod to drown the silence and lighten the mood. Beyoncé's "Run the World (Girls)" was playing, ironically. We sang every word out loud, until we dropped my mom at her house.

At home, Blossom ran through the French doors to the backyard and found a sunny spot next to the deck. Though the grass was still a bit damp from the rain shower, she laid down on it anyway. I wanted to take her a blanket, but it was too late.

From the window, I watched her looking at the sky. With her right hand, Blossom traced her fingers over her face, breasts, and hair. Then she exhaled. I could tell that she had closed her eyes. I walked away to start preparing dinner. I knew she needed this moment alone.

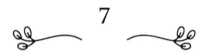

7

Replaying every moment in my mind, from the night I started dreaming of my dad, through the changes to my body, to learning I would receive a power; rubbing my fingers over the sharp blades of grass, knocking the translucent droplets of rain off one by one; I slowly stood up. My back was wet from the grass. I held my head back so the sun could keep warming my body. The rays burned but felt good. There was a slight breeze, and the sweetness of our garden pierced my nose.

I felt Momma's eyes on me from the kitchen window. I wanted to be alone, so I headed toward the tall oak tree that held my treehouse. I hadn't noticed until now, but the treehouse was in desperate need of repainting. I'll call Poppy later so he can help me fix it up.

I reached out my index finger to touch the wildflowers that covered every step of the ladder and the vines that wrapped around the tree trunk. I felt a *zap* race through my entire body. For a second, I thought a bee had stung me, but there wasn't a stinger in my finger nor any bees around, so I started climbing the ladder, until I felt another zap.

Pausing on the fourth step and looking at each of my fingers in turn, I saw sparkles dancing around the flowers. Wide-eyed, I could only mouth *oh no!* Because the words wouldn't come out.

I hurried down the ladder, skipping the last two steps to jump to the grass. Curious, I touched one of the wildflowers surrounding the oak tree, and it began to transform. After a few seconds, it was a rose.

"Cool!" I touched another wildflower, and this one turned into an iris. With each touch, another blossom transformed. I scurried back up the ladder, on a mission now to retrieve the *Nova Book of Magic*.

Breathless, I pulled the book down from the third-row shelf. There were still pieces of mud dried onto some of the pages from being buried so long. Taking a seat on my favorite purple rug, I started flipping through it.

The floorboards creaked, and I turned around in time to see my momma's fingers pulling open the door.

"I was calling your name. Time for dinner."

"Sorry, Momma. I didn't hear you."

"It's OK. I knew where to find you. Did you know there's a trail of sparkles leading up to your door?"

"No, but I know where they came from! I have a new power, and it's so cool!"

Momma followed me back down the ladder to the grass. The sparkles were disappearing, and the flowers I had changed were now wildflowers again.

"Watch," I said, pointing at the top of a purple wildflower. I touched it and counted to five as it turned into a hydrangea.

Momma's eyes sparkled a bright silver.

"Well, watch this, Blossom!" She wiped her eye with a fingertip and rubbed her tears on the hydrangea. It started to sparkle.

"It's so pretty!"

"I used to go behind Poppy as he was landscaping in Sibley Park and add something special to his flowers."

"You have more than one power too?"

"Not necessarily. It's sort of an added bonus. I learned how to do it from the *Nova Book of Magic*."

It dawned on me that Momma had never told me what powers she and Granny had. The changes in my life were so consuming that I selfishly hadn't asked the one person who could relate to them. Momma always tells her friends on the phone to stop bottling things up and to talk to someone they trust. I guess it's time to take the advice that I've overheard many times.

"Well, B, I can control the rain to some degree."

"Some degree? You either control it or you don't." I was so confused.

"Haven't you noticed that it only rains when I cry?"

"I knew it!"

And suddenly it all made sense. The weird rainstorms at night when I heard her crying. The rain when we're at the park. "Is that why you pinch your arms?"

"Yes, to stop myself from crying. I know it's stupid, but the *Nova Book of Magic* didn't have any instructions beyond saying that my tears would *produce rain, floods, and occasional storms.*"

"Did you ever start crying to avoid going to school?"

"No, B. I loved school. My powers are just useful for plants, flowers and trees, I guess. It would never rain in Anastasia if it weren't for me. But I'll give God some credit too," she laughed. "When Granny Lily told me that I would get a superpower, I was nervous, excited, and curious. Being the shy girl in school wasn't always easy. I was never the popular girl or the dork, but I did a great job of just blending in. Having a power made me feel unique. I was finally more than the smart, pretty, wallflower, who wrote for *The Scout*. That was my school newspaper."

"You have a pretty important power, Momma."

"I do. It's just not as cool as yours," she said, tickling my side. "I mean, when I cry, it rains. If they are happy tears, or sad or excited tears, that determines how it rains."

I thought about that. The *Nova Book of Magic* had been teaching me a lot about my powers too. And lately I noticed that more pages had appeared in it. Could that mean I was getting another power? *Duh!* I smacked myself on the forehead. Of course. I do have two powers now. I can't wait to read about the new one.

I remembered that I hadn't seen anything about mom or Granny Lily's powers in the book. "What happens if your power isn't in the book any longer?"

"Are you asking why my power isn't in the book?"

I nodded. I couldn't make any words come out. These days I've been finding myself speechless a lot.

"I tore them out before your daddy died. It doesn't mean I'll lose them. Or at least, I don't think it does. Maybe I'll receive another power later in life. No one really knows. I guess we'll just wait and see."

Momma was lying. I could tell. Like Poppy, she would make a sniffling noise and avoid eye contact. But I didn't have the energy to question her, so I let her stick with that story. Maybe it was best that I didn't know. I changed the direction of the conversation back to her power.

"Is that how you got your name?"

"My name is coincidental. Well, sort of." She explained that when she was born and let out her first cry, a storm started out of nowhere. It was night and dark outside, but Granny Lily's hospital room had lots of windows, and the lightening was so intense it looked like daylight. The louder Momma's screams got, the worse the storm grew. But as soon as Granny Lily managed to pacify her, it stopped. Poppy had been looking out of the window, anxious about the birth of his first child but also because there hadn't been rain in the forecast for Anastasia in more than a year. It was at that moment that Poppy and Granny Lily knew momma was special. They didn't know that rain was her actual power until puberty. That was the same day Poppy gained his power as well.

I thought back to all the times it had rained in my life, and *boom!* It made sense of all the mysterious weather changes when momma became emotional.

The worst storms happened when she cried because she missed my dad. Those times, the rain was heavy. When she got emotional during a movie, or even happy about me accomplishing something at school, clouds would move in quickly and small drops would splash to the ground.

It was rare to see Momma cry, and now I knew why. It wasn't because she was awkward or lacked emotion, but because she was afraid of the damage she could cause.

"I knew it!" I said. "I just couldn't explain it."

Momma flashed me a smile that I hadn't seen in a long time. I could tell she was relieved to finally be able to tell someone about her power. We've always been close, but this secret had suddenly brought us even closer. My heart felt a little funny thinking about it.

Before she revealed her secret to me, she said, only Poppy, Granny Lily, and Daddy had known of her power. There were rumors around town, but no one was bold enough ask. And there were pictures all over the internet, but no actual evidence. Our family had to make sure our secret never got out.

"So, we're more alike than you thought, baby." Momma winked, and I caught it in my hand, closed my eyes, blew the wink, and made a wish like I always do.

"I can't wait to learn more about this power."

"Me too. But first, let's eat."

I grabbed Momma's hand and we skipped back to the house. The day had taken a lot of my energy, but was turning out to be one of the best days ever. It was great having someone who knew what I was going through.

Because school was starting, and I wanted to play sports, Momma made an appointment for me with my doctor. Like usual, she checked my temperature, made me take off my shoes to step on the cold scale, and put that itchy cuff around my arm to check my blood pressure. And she gave me the worst news ever. Dr. Greystone told my mom and me that she expected I would get my period within the next year.

I know it's supposed to happen at some point, but I'm not ready. Hearing my doctor say it just made the reality even scarier. I mean, doctors know everything.

Momma stayed calm, but I could tell she was just as nervous as me. All her emotions were in her silver eyes.

Dr. Greystone left the room, so I could get dressed, and as I put on my jeans, my mom cleared her throat.

"B, when did you start growing hair down there?"

I felt my face grow hot. "Maybe a few weeks ago."

"You didn't notice any other changes?" Momma's eyes grew wide with dread.

"No!" I felt a sense of relief. Maybe I won't get another power. Momma sat back in her chair, exhaling.

Between dealing with these stupid lumps on my chest, the itchy hair sprouting in my underwear, and my new superpowers, I'm becoming a mess. Last week, I got in trouble when Momma caught me using her razor to shave all the hair that had grown under my arms and on my legs. I was getting ready to shave my twinker too, when I got caught.

I can't bring myself to say the v-word. Since I can remember, I've always referred to my private area as my twinker. Momma never corrected me on a lot of words, because she thought the way I said them was cute.

I never saw her so angry as when she caught me. We had just discussed my hair growth and decided that I could start shaving in sixth grade, but I took it upon myself to start early. Emma had told me that if I started shaving before the hair grew in down there, then it wouldn't grow at all. Clearly that was a lie.

I hate that whenever I do something wrong, Momma has to call everyone and tell them my business. But this time she didn't. It started thundering so loud outside that I couldn't understand what she was yelling. It was sunny before she walked into the bathroom and now, a storm came out of nowhere.

The more my body changes, the more I want privacy. I've even found myself covering up more, and I'm not sure why. It's just weird having your body change and not being able to control it. I wish I could use my powers to slow it down.

As I tied my shoelaces, Momma stood up, but she stopped a few inches from the door. "I think we should go buy some feminine products today, so you can be ready."

I covered my eyes with my hands.

"What if I start my, you know what, at school? What if I get another superpower?"

"Oh, baby, I didn't even think about that. I guess we'll have to cross that bridge when we come to it. Hopefully you'll start at home, but Dr. Greystone says we still have some time. For now, let's get to the store. Maybe we can find a cute little purse so you can carry your pads discreetly."

"Good idea, Momma."

"Look on the bright side, B. Poppy had to buy my first pack of pads, because Granny Lily was out of town when I got my ruby."

"How embarrassing."

"It wasn't embarrassing, just a little awkward. I expected to have that moment with Granny Lily. Poppy was clueless, so I had to call my friends to find out what to do. Like, how often do I change the pad? Will I die if I lose too much blood? Stuff like that."

"I guess we sort of have similar experiences, since Daddy gives me gifts that represent my changes and powers. He knows when I'll start my ruby before anyone."

Mom just looked down, nervous, pinching her arm.

In my heart, I thought none of this was a good idea. Everyone would know that I'd gotten my period if I pulled out a random purse that I never carried to school. I hope I never start my period, ruby, or whatever it's called. Well, at least not anytime soon.

8

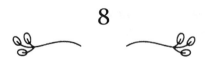

Since I was three years old and first had enough hair to put in a ponytail, Momma would place a single braid around my hairline. She's no hairstylist, but she's gotten good at it over the years. I love when she brushes through my curls or scratches my scalp before she washes my hair. Momma says my hair is her favorite part of me. Sometimes I think she knows how many strands of hair I have on my head. She runs her fingers through my hair every night until I fall asleep.

I get compliments all the time. People always stop and ask, "Where did she get all that hair from?" Momma always giggles and replies, "I'm still trying to figure that out myself." If Momma would let me talk to strangers, I'd say "Not from the store, like you get yours!" Unfortunately, I have to be polite and smile because I'm just a kid.

Today is the first time in my life that I'm getting my hair flat-ironed. Mom wants me to look beautiful for the first day of sixth grade. Mrs. Joy always does Momma's hair and makes her look like a movie star. I can't wait to look like her.

Mrs. Joy shampooed my hair, like always. She oohed and awed and teased me, saying she was going to cut all my hair off one day and put it on her own head. She's so silly. After sitting me under the dryer for what seemed like hours, she started to prep me for the flat iron. I was so excited that I could barely keep still in the chair. Momma watched with stern eyes and warned me that I would get burnt if I kept moving.

On the first stroke through my hair, I heard a sizzle and a pop and saw smoke blowing all around my head.

"Momma, am I on fire?"

"No, baby, it's just smoke from the flat iron. You're OK."

I gripped the armrests of the black leather chair. What would I do if my hair did catch fire? It would take ten years to grow back. I couldn't imagine starting school bald.

It's hard enough keeping my new power a secret. Mrs. Joy has a beautiful bouquet of wild daisies from her husband on the side table by the magazines that I would love to change into tie-dye daisies. But Momma won't let me change flowers in public places, even when we're the only two around.

Lost in my thoughts, I almost forgot Mrs. Joy was doing my hair.

It took her maybe two minutes to get through the first strand. Then I heard her whisper something to Momma, but I couldn't make it out. Momma set her gold sketchbook on the counter and darted behind my chair. I could tell from their facial expressions in the mirror that something was wrong, but I was afraid to move. I closed my eyes, gripped the armrests tighter, and braced myself for the bad news.

"Oh, my goodness!"

"What is it, Momma? I'm bald, aren't I?" I mistook the wetness on my face for tears, but when huge drops fell from my face onto the leopard print cape protecting my new denim jumper, I realized I was actually sweating. Staring at the blank phone screen in my hand, I noticed that my eyes had changed from hazel to green, like they always do when I'm upset.

"No, Blossom. Look!"

Mrs. Joy held up the hand-mirror so I could see the back of my head. At first, I thought I was dreaming, but I could see little rainbow sparkles dancing on the now-straight strands of hair.

"Mrs. Joy, you just sprayed glitter on my hair," I said, laughing and wiping the sweat from my face with the back of my hand. She was always playing jokes on me. But then I realized that the sparkles were just like the ones that had followed me up the ladder when I discovered that I could change flowers with my fingertips.

"Honey, I've just been flat-ironing." Mrs. Joy seemed nervous. She walked over to the small table with the bouquet, picked out a wild daisy, and brought it back. "Here, honey. I know you like flowers. How about you hold onto it until I'm finished. I don't need you sweating out this gorgeous hair before we're done."

When I was younger, Mrs. Joy would always let me take one of her flowers home. I don't know if it was to prevent me from breaking the vase or because she knew how much I loved flowers. She also knew Poppy and would sometimes wash his hair and trim his beard, and they would talk about landscaping and how I would always take seeds home and plant them in our garden. Then Mrs. Joy would always ask me to bring her a flower when Momma had a hair appointment. Today I forgot to bring one.

I smiled and thanked her. Momma winked at me but also gave a look that didn't need words to follow. I knew that meant to try my hardest not to change the daisy into another flower. If I kept the stem away from my index fingers, I wouldn't be able to change it.

Momma looked nervous, but she assured Mrs. Joy that everything would be fine. Then she sat down and started texting very fast. I'm pretty sure she was texting Granny Lily for an excuse to give Mrs. Joy, so our family secret wouldn't get out. Granny Lily knows everything, and I was sure she'd come up with something clever.

Several minutes went by and Granny Lily still hadn't replied. I could tell Momma was getting nervous because she was picking invisible lint off her blue maxi dress. I decided to end the awkward silence.

"Mrs. Joy probably forgot she bought the sparkle hair products from that gift shop in Disneyland last summer."

Searching the salon with my eyes, I remembered that her daughter had put a bottle of glitter hairspray under the sink.

"Mrs. Joy, I'm still sweating. Could you please get me a drink of water?"

She paused, still confused about what was happening with my hair, and then said "Of course, honey. I'll be right back."

After the door shut behind her, I jumped up to grab the hairspray from below the sink and switched it with the silver bottle she was using. I made it back to the chair just as she opened the door carrying three bottles of water.

Without saying a word, Mrs. Joy continued straightening my hair. She hadn't noticed the replacement bottle, and she started spraying small sections of my hair. Soon glitter was blowing everywhere. Mom and I connected eyes, and she smirked and pretended to look for something in her purse.

In the mirror, I saw Mrs. Joy pause, take a step back, and then burst into laughter.

"Oh, my goodness! How did I not notice that I was using glitter hairspray on your hair? My daughter must have been playing around with my products."

"Whelp, that explains everything. You made me nervous, Mrs. Joy."

"You almost had me believing my Blossom had magical powers or something," Momma laughed nervously.

After two hours, my hair was finished. And there was so much of it! It was a lot longer straight than curly, I guess due to that black girl magic everyone talks about.

"I love it, Mrs. Joy!"

She sprayed my hair again, this time with the spray I had put under the sink. I told my hair over and over in my head to stay straight. Since what had happened was so new, I still didn't know how to control it, or even what kind of power it was.

Mrs. Joy looked a bit confused after taking the leopard cape from around my body, but she said nothing. I was still clutching the wild daisy underneath, careful to make a fist, so my fingertips wouldn't touch the stem. In my nervousness, I hadn't noticed that the multi-colored wild daisy had already changed into a beautiful tie-dyed lily, and when I saw it, I remembered reading in the *Nova Book of Magic* that water could also make flowers change.

While Momma paid, I managed to change the lily back without Mrs. Joy noticing. When she turned around to give me a hug, she paused, confusion written all over her face. I kissed her on the cheek.

"Enjoy your first day of school. Don't forget to send pictures," Mrs. Joy said as she waved goodbye.

Momma grabbed my hand and we headed for the door. I turned, remembering that I had left the flower on the chair, and I saw Mrs. Joy inspecting it. My face felt hot, but I headed toward our SUV, afraid to tell Momma.

Sitting in the back seat, I remembered that I hadn't gotten a visit from my Dad. I'd fallen asleep in Momma's bed last night. She had been binge watching old episodes of Gilmore Girls while sketching dresses for her upcoming fashion show. I decided to make sure I made it to my own bed every night. I couldn't take any more surprises—this had been a close one.

When we got home, I had just enough energy to put a scarf on to protect my hair. All I remember after that is pulling my blanket over my head. Then I closed my eyes, entering the magical world where I see daddy.

Usually we meet in my bedroom, but this time we met in the treehouse. Dad was sitting on the little cherrywood table in the corner, reading a book. The chairs were too small for his large legs. Poppy said it's time for him to make me a new set, since I've started bumping my knees under the table.

"Dad!" I ran and jumped into his arms, nearly knocking him over.

"Dad? Not Daddy? B, you've grown so much since I last saw you."

I've had a hard time dealing with my new powers, so I've been sleeping in Mom's bed lately, where my dad can't visit me. But I've decided to pull out my dollhouse anytime I feel scared or anxious. A lot of my friends make fun of my old dolls and dollhouse, but I find great joy in escaping to an imaginary world with my toys. There are days when I feel like I'm too old to play with them, but then I think of Poppy and Dad asking me to remain a little girl as long as I can.

I'm in no rush to grow up. From what I hear, being a grown up isn't that exciting. Mom always smiles when she walks past my room and sees me playing. I hear her telling her friends that she knows when I've had a bad day at school, because I head straight for the dollhouses in my closet. I wish my emotions were less obvious. Having to deal with powers now, I'm a mess.

I didn't even notice that I'd called him Dad, but it sounded a lot more grownup coming out. Dad hugged me again and asked about Mom. I know he misses her a lot. He always gets choked up when he speaks about her. My parents haven't had any contact in the dream realm. My dad always tells me how much he misses me, but I know he would give anything to see my mom again.

"She's fine, but she's taking my growing up a little hard. She's always pinching her arms, Dad. Some nights I can hear her crying, but then the raindrops get so loud they drown it out."

Dad was smiling through his tears. It's weird, but I love his smile. It always puts me at ease.

"Sorry, Dad. This whole power thing isn't as exciting as I thought it would be. It's kind of scary. I don't want to mess up and reveal our secret to the world."

Dad just stood in silence, wishing he could be there for us. He couldn't stop hugging me, either, but he pulled back for a second to trace his fingers over my face.

His sadness was starting to make me upset. We don't have much time together in my dreams, so I told him what Poppy said about my dreams being real. He didn't look shocked. He just said, "I know."

"Who told you, Da—Daddy?

I could feel the sun warming my skin and the backs of my eyelids turning orange. I hadn't even gotten to tell him about my new powers. But by the look on his face, I could tell he already knew. Before my dream ended, I whispered in his ear that I would call him Daddy forever. It was bad enough he couldn't experience life with me every day. The least I could do was give him a little longer with his little girl.

This time Daddy didn't say "I love you," he just handed me a rope with a rose tied to the end. Then he kissed my forehead and mumbled something in my ear, but all I could only make out was "change." Then I woke up hearing myself say "Forever and always."

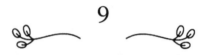

9

The next morning, I couldn't wait to remove my silk scarf so I could brush my long, straight hair before Mom woke up. Next to my pillow was the rope Daddy gave me in my dream. I'm not sure what it means, but I have more exciting business at hand. I unraveled the mummy wrapping from my head, pulled my new hairbrush out of the drawer, and began to brush the long strands. The first stroke felt like silk thrown down to me from heaven. I brushed all the way down to my waist. But then something weird happened.

One section of my hair began to stand up on its own and recoil. Terrified, I brushed another piece to make sure I wasn't imaging things. That strand stood straight up too, almost touching the ceiling, and then recoiled, falling onto my back.

I screamed, dropped my brush, and ran to Mom's bedroom.

"Mom, Momma, Mommy, please get up!" Desperate, I started shaking her by the shoulders.

Mom opened her eyes, still groggy. "What's wrong, Blossom? Did you have a bad dream?"

"No, Mom, look!" I pointed to the two curls on my head.

Mom looked mad, but politely asked if I'd gotten my hair wet in the shower.

"No! I just brushed it, Mom. I swear!"

I ran to the gold mirror near her closet door. My hair was no longer standing upright on top of my head. There were just two curls sticking straight up. No wonder she thought I'd gotten it wet.

"Mom, my hair did something when I was in the bathroom."

Mom sat up again, rubbing her eyes. "Show me what happened."

I could tell she didn't believe me, so I grabbed a brush out of her vanity and started brushing my hair again. With each stroke, a strand of my golden-brown hair stood up on my head. Three thick locks twined themselves into a braid while the rest of my hair coiled and uncoiled like serpents dancing for a snake charmer.

Mom's eyes grew wide. "It's happening, baby."

Together we said, "Superpower!"

Mom drew the curtains from her bay window to see if anything was happening outside, but we saw nothing unusual.

Pacing back and forth, Mom looked nervous but excited. I was just nervous. Finally, she gently touched the braid that had formed in my hair. She gulped.

"Mom, what's happening?"

"Your hair moved on its own." She looked stunned, but she stretched out her right hand to touch my hair again.

This time the braid coiled itself around her arm. I could see what was happening in the mirror. I didn't want my hair to hurt Mom, so I closed my eyes and whispered, "Please let go." I opened my eyes and just like that, my braid released her arm and fell back into place in the rest of my hair.

"I did it!"

"You did what?" Mom asked, stunned.

"I politely asked my hair to let go of your arm and it did."

"B, I think your new power is in your hair. Try telling it to grab this brush." She picked up the gold brush from her vanity and held it out.

I closed my eyes again, this time saying, "Grab the brush."

I opened one eye to see what is happening. Small golden bits of glitter like the ones that had appeared when Mrs. Joy straightened my hair, and when I healed Theo, floated around my braid, lifting it away from my face. The end of the braid coiled around the handle of the brush, pulling it out of Mom's hand. We stared at one another.

"This is so cool! It doesn't even hurt."

"I have to call your granny."

That night, I closed my eyes and entered the place where I see Daddy. I was so excited to tell him about my new power. When I opened my eyes in the dream world, there he was, sitting in the purple zebra-striped chair by my desk.

"It's about time my big girl showed up. I was getting worried." He stood up to give me a hug.

"Sorry, Daddy. Mom let me stay up longer tonight, since we discovered something."

"Like treasure?" Daddy laughed, tickling me.

"I wish! Daddy, you might want to sit down."

Daddy sat on the end of my bed, but not before hitting his head on the new chandelier Mom and I had hung up earlier. "What's going on, honey?"

"Daddy, I have a third power!"

"Hm. I think it has something to do with the rope I gave you."

"It does. I tried to tell you the other night, but you were really upset."

"Being trapped in your dreams, I learn about what's going on in your life ahead of time. I thought you were supposed to get one power once you got your period, but you seem to be an exception. Perhaps you're a *Super Nova*. Before I gave you the rope, it was given to me by the Dream Keeper."

"A *Super Nova*? Like, I'm a Nova with superpowers?"

"Yea, something like that. I'll need to do more research."

All of this seemed unbelievable but considering what I'd been through over the past year, nothing surprises me now. Still, I sat speechless with my mouth open wide. I finally closed it after feeling my tongue getting dry.

Daddy continued to speak. "I figured out that the gifts are clues to your superpowers, but I never know what type of power you'll receive."

"My new power is in my hair. Watch this."

I told my hair to grab hold of Daddy's arm. The sparkles appeared, and my hair split into three sections and started to braid itself.

Daddy almost fell off the bed. He held out his right arm to keep from falling, and my long braid coiled snugly around it, catching Daddy, and pulling him back up.

"Well, I guess that does explain the rope," he said, with his eyes open wide. Like mine, his eyes got lighter when he was sad or excited. "I know we don't have much time. What are your other powers?"

"I can change flowers."

The room started to grow lighter. We both knew the sun was a sign that our meeting was about to end. I told my hair to release Daddy's arm, and he knelt beside of my bed and kissed me on the cheek. Then he carefully pulled a shimmering golden box from underneath the bed. This was the first time he gave me a gift and wasn't crying.

"Am I getting another power?"

"Maybe. I think you'll really like this one." He winked.

If I received another power, I had no idea where it would come from. Nothing else about me had changed lately. I hoped my infamous "ruby" wasn't starting.

With trembling hands, I unwrapped the box. Inside was a jeweled mirror with an amaryllis flower engraved on the back. I learned the names of every flower from Poppy. Before he retired, Poppy had been the only landscaper in Anastasia. When I was three, he started taking me with him on some of his jobs. Since I was learning to read at the time, Poppy thought it was only right for me to learn the names of the flowers and plants too. He said it would help with my colors and vocabulary.

All my daddy could say was, "I love you, beautiful."

"Forever and always."

He never says "beautiful." I mean, I know he thinks I am, but we have a thing. He says, "I love you," and I say, "Forever and always."

10

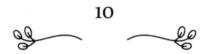

I am now ten and a half. I woke up before Mom to brush my teeth and wash my face. I stopped calling her Momma after my second power appeared. She didn't make a big deal of it, like Daddy.

I get to play on the computer longer if Mom doesn't have to ask me to get ready. Turning the hot water on first, I squirted a penny-sized drop of cleanser into my hand and in a circular motion, began to apply it to my face just like Granny Lily taught me. I don't ever want wrinkles like some of the old ladies at church have, so I take advice from the prettiest old lady I know. Shh, don't tell her I called her old.

Ouch!

Either the cleanser burned me, or I forgot to turn the cold water on again. I was afraid of opening my eyes too fast because last time the soap got in and I couldn't see for an hour. So, I waited a few minutes, making sure the soap was cleared from my eyes so I could see where the burning sensation was coming from, and there it—*ouch!*

Even the touch of my fingers seemed to zap my skin.

I was sure I put my hand sanitizer under the sink. Last time I mistook it for soap, and that was a disaster.

"Mom! Mom—Mom!"

Mom ran into my room after hearing my screams. "Blossom, what is it?"

"I think I have chicken pox, but just one itchy bump is on my face."

Mom burst into laughter. "Let me see." She moved my face side to side, with my chin pinched between her index finger and thumb. "Baby, you have a pimple."

"A pimple! I wash my face every day—well, almost every day—like you ask." I'm not old enough to get pimples. Am I?

"B, this is a part of the change I was telling you about. Did anything else happen after you touched your face?"

With tears in my eyes, I simply said "No." Kids and teens in movies typically get teased. I've been somewhat popular in school, and I don't want to start getting teased. I'd never seen this happen to anyone at school, but some kids were mean, and girls like Sarah and Ashley were always making rude comments about others.

Mom wiped my tears away just like she always does, but this time something strange happened. When I saw the look on her face, my first reaction was to jump up and look out the window.

This couldn't be another power. Novas only get one power, and I already had three. I was only just learning to control the power in my hair. I strained my eyes to see anything outside, but I didn't know what to look for.

"What now?" Then I remembered my dream from last night. "Daddy told me that the gifts he gives me represent a superpower."

"What else did he say?"

"He said that he never knows what the power will be. Like us, he thought I would only get one power. He didn't promise that I'd receive another, but whatever it is, I would like it. Mom, what kind of power do you think this pimple will bring?"

Mom stood motionless, maybe because she was hoping Daddy asked about her, or because she was curious to learn about another power. Maybe she could already see my new power. But she's not saying anything and it's driving me crazy.

"You are rare, baby. I only got one superpower with puberty. And a bonus, but that doesn't really count. You seem to have four." Mom snapped out of whatever trance she was just in. "Honestly, Blossom, I don't think you're going to find your power outside."

"What do you mean? Did something happen in my room?" I searched every corner with my eyes. Nothing was out of place, nor had anything new appeared.

Maybe I didn't get a power with this pimple. A sigh of relief passed through me, but I couldn't get past the way she was looking at me.

"Sunshine, look in the mirror."

I took a big gulp before walking over to the floor-length mirror Granny Lily had helped me glue blue and green gems to the border of, last summer. She got the cool design from Pinterest. Before reaching it, I stopped, and turned to look at her. Perhaps for reassurance, or perhaps for that fact that my feet wouldn't move forward.

"Mom, I can't do this. I'm scared."

Feelings of confusion and fear started to take over. Trying to change the subject, I asked about Granny Lily's power.

"Granny's power isn't nature related like most of the Nova women, and now you. She can hear everyone's thoughts."

"Is that why Granny Lily always says 'Blossom, you'd better not' when she thinks I'm going to be sassy?"

Mom laughed. "That's exactly why! I couldn't get away with anything as a teenager.

"And Poppy?"

Poppy developed his power after I was born. He's clairvoyant, which means he can see things before they happen. He can't see everything because he trained himself not to. It was making him crazy to see so many things. So, now he just pays attention to certain visions."

"Like what?"

"He picks and chooses. Let's just say Poppy knew I would marry your daddy, and he also knew that Daddy would die. The bad thing is that Poppy doesn't know when something is going to happen. He just knows it will, eventually."

I went from being excited to a ball of shock, confusion, and questions. "Did my dad have a power?"

Mom looked away. Her lips quivered as she spoke. "Your dad never had a power, per se. His curse, as I like to call it, was in the way that he loved. He loved us so much that his heart gave out."

"My dad had a heart attack?"

"Kind of. Poppy had a vision that your dad would die after we conceived you. I'm not sure about all the rules of magic, but it had something to do with our being Novas, and our first child being a girl."

"I killed my dad?"

"No, honey! Don't you ever say that! If that were the case Poppy and every man in our family would have died too."

"I killed him."

"What?"

Bit by bit, I backed away. "Is this why Grandma and Grandpa Brenton refuse to see me?"

She shook her head. "They're angry with me, Blossom, not you. I learned about what could happen to your dad on our wedding day. We'd never talked about having children, but before we conceived you, having a child was heavy on my mind. In Nova history, the firstborn children are always girls, so the chances were slim that we'd have a boy first. After hearing that, all I wanted was to have a part of Erick. I was selfish—I'd rather have something than nothing at all. And out of anger and sadness, I told someone about our family secret. I told Suri, before I could stop myself. I know Suri will take our secret to the grave, but I later learned—in that stupid book—that I, I . . . I sealed your dad's fate by telling someone about our magic. There are major consequences to that. Mine was your dad dying. I lied to you, Blossom—about why I tore some pages out of the *Nova Book of Magic*. Those pages are still buried under the cherry blossom tree. They reveal what I did."

Mom was crying now. The rain started to pour down. Usually when she cries, the raindrops are soft and then get stronger if she can't stop herself. This time, the rain was accompanied by thunder so loud that I could hardly hear anything she was saying. But I couldn't speak to tell her to talk louder.

My eyes were full of tears. My heartbeat sped up and wouldn't slow down again. I could see Mom's mouth moving, but my ears could no longer hear. It was as if seashells were covering them, and I could only hear the wind. I cuffed my ears, hoping to hear the rest of the story. I don't know if my hurt exploded and clogged my ears, or if the information was too much for my brain to handle.

Mom must have noticed my confusion because she stopped talking and just stood still. The sorrow in her eyes made me want to run and hug her, but I still couldn't move. My wild hair began to stretch and weave itself into two intricate French braids. I didn't command it to do anything. I just stood there, powerless. My fingertips burned hot. I looked down, and the tiny gold and silver sparkles that always show up when I use my powers had appeared. I didn't instruct my body to do anything, yet all of this was happening.

The scent of flowers filled my nostrils, sweet yet overwhelming. Wildflowers, roses, hydrangeas—I stopped keeping track of what was appearing in my room. From the corner of my eye, I saw Mom backing away. Her mouth was moving, but I still couldn't hear the words.

Not wanting a bunch of injured animals to start clawing at my windows like some kind of zombie apocalypse, I closed my eyes so tight that my eyelids twitched, hoping everything would stop. After counting to ten, I opened my eyes and found my powers had stopped working on their own.

I held out my hand and told my mom, still standing on the far side of my room, to walk toward me. What she said about my dad's death must have had something to do with my powers going out of whack.

My mom forced herself away from the wall and walked toward me. Grabbing both my hands and kissing me on the forehead, she asked if I was OK. I nodded my head yes.

"Can you hear me?"

Again, I could only nod.

"You have nothing to worry about. Whatever powers these changes bring, I will be here to help you control them. I know what I just told you was a lot to take in, but we'll get through it. Together."

I didn't want to tell her that I hadn't heard anything after she said my dad's heart gave out. Maybe that was all I wanted to hear. She seemed relieved after talking, and I didn't want to ruin the moment.

Staring into my eyes, Mom could see that I didn't want to talk about it any further. The corners of her mouth twitched as she smiled. Her eyes were nervous, as if she could hear my thoughts. I hope she didn't forget to tell me that she was a mind reader too, like Granny Lily, or else I'm screwed.

The rain stopped, along with the thunder. Through my window, I could see that most of the garden was mud. I'd call Poppy later to come help us plant new flowers. But considering that he has eyes and ears, I was pretty sure he was on the way already.

"Mom, I have something to tell you."

My mom knew I was trying to stall her and forget about what just happened, so she grabbed my shoulders and turned me toward the mirror. But before I could see our reflections, she placed her hands over my eyes.

"When I count to three, I'm going to take my hands away and you'll be able to see your power."

"OK."

Inhaling, she counted and then removed her hands. I took a moment before looking up at myself in the mirror. The pimple was no longer visible.

"Mom, do you see me?"

I've never paid much attention to my looks. I barely notice whether my shoes match. Mom always stresses the importance of self-esteem and self-love, so I never worry about looks. She explains how everyone has insecurities and no one is perfect, so I just lived life accordingly, not really caring what others thought of me. I'd rather be known for being smart, like Mom, than for being beautiful. But my family and the townspeople were always telling me how beautiful I was, and for once I now see what they were talking about.

"Yes, gorgeous, I see you! You're beautiful—well even more beautiful, just like Daddy said in your dream."

I traced my green sparkle-covered nails over my new facial features. "Is it possible to have a power to make yourself more beautiful?"

"It seems that anything is possible. Maybe this isn't a power, exactly."

"Do you think that every time I get a pimple, I'll become even more beautiful?"

"I'm not sure, sunshine. We'll just have to keep track." Then she held up her index finger, signaling me to hold my thought, before she left my room.

While Mom left to get her phone, I remained at the mirror. I still looked like the girl who was there just an hour ago washing my face, but older now and more beautiful. My bronze skin glowed, enhancing the sandy color of my curls. My hazel eyes had grown brighter and more intense. The unibrow that my mom waxed every month was gone, and in the place of my hair caterpillar, as Poppy used to joke, were two perfectly sculpted eyebrows. Instead of the little button nose that everyone loved to kiss, was a straighter, more adult nose that resembled Mom's.

The crescent-shaped dimple on my left cheek was more defined. I put my finger into it, smiling brightly. I had gotten that one misplaced dimple from my daddy. When he smiled, the same half-moon shape would appear.

I looked carefully over the rest of my body. Nothing else had changed. My armpits where smooth, because Mom had finally started letting me shave them after I was teased at school. I had raised my hand to answer a question, and one of the immature new boys said my armpits looked like the hair on the floor at the barbershop. I also got to shave my legs too. Mom comes in the bathroom and shaves hers at the same time, making a fun mess out of the shaving cream.

I've been noticing more pubic hair and have been shaving it behind Mom's back. I promised to not do that without speaking to her, but it's so awkward, especially when I wear a bathing suit. I guess now, isn't a good time to bring it up.

I wish Daddy were here to see me grow up. Well, minus the pubic hair part. Before I could get lost in thoughts about Daddy, Mom returned with her iPhone.

"I'm going to start documenting your changes. Luckily, we took pictures yesterday, so we'll be able to point out the differences."

I love taking pictures, so this was going to be fun.

Mom backed me up to my door, the single blank surface in my room, and told me to say "Nova." The flash was blinding. Then when Mom looked down at the image, she dropped the phone, shattering the screen.

"We need to dig up the missing pages."

When I was sixteen, I dreamt that I met the most handsome man in the world. He stood about six-foot-four and had sun-kissed skin like my own and these unforgettable hazel eyes that flickered like embers when he smiled. He had beautiful white teeth that I couldn't take my eyes off.

I was sitting under the famous cherry blossom tree in Sibley Park when he approached. In the dream, I was older than sixteen, but all my surroundings were very familiar, maybe because I went to the park every day, rain, or shine. Since I can control the precipitation, the sun was always shining.

A very handsome man approached me. He seemed a bit nervous, but he had a confident handshake. I'm generally shy—that's how I know it was a dream because I asked him to sit beside me. I had more confidence than anyone in the world.

That's a scary thought, considering how much a wallflower I am. I make better drapes than a coffee table, if you catch my drift. Bad analogy, but you get my point. Rain Nova would rather blend into the background than be the life of the party.

When the mystery man was with me, nothing else mattered. Everything felt familiar, but foreign, and fated. Our meeting was magical, or maybe it was just the soap opera fog of the dream that clouded my judgment. Honestly, this fragment of my imagination is one reason I didn't start dating until I was twenty-one. I never felt the same magic with anyone else like I did with the man in my dream.

My parents never had to worry about me being boy crazy. High school boys scared me. It was weird for me to even have a dream like that. Maybe my subconscious was trying to tell me something. Or I could be overthinking life, as usual.

11

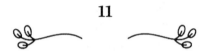

I was twenty-four when I met the beautiful Rain Nova. She was like no one I'd ever known. Her beauty was inexplicable. If anyone was asked to describe Rain in one word, they would simply say "stunning."

From the moment I first saw Rain sitting alone in Sibley Park under the cherry blossom tree, I knew that one day she would be my wife. Her hair was in a purposeful messy bun. She wore black Lycra leggings and a bright pink sports bra. She even had on the pink version of my black and white Nike Zoom Victory running shoes.

There was something captivating about her eyes. Not just the color of smoldering silver, but the way she stared into my soul when I first approached to say hello. She gave me chills, even when she shyly looked away. Love at first sight would be an understatement. I was more intrigued than I had ever been by another person. Rain's smile was reassuring, and her confidence seemed to burst through her fingertips. If it's possible to have an out-of-body experience without being close to death, then that's exactly what was happening between us. If I didn't know any better, I'd say something magical happened under the only cherry blossom tree in Sibley Park.

Rain noticed me staring, and to make the moment less awkward she patted the space next to her on the bench. "Have a seat."

I stumbled a bit because I couldn't believe this beautiful freak of nature was so willing to invite me into her world. Her perfect smile was warm and inviting. I hoped my face didn't reveal my thoughts. I considered myself a ladies' man, but Rain seemed out of my league.

"I'm Rain."

"Hello beautiful, I'm Erick."

We talked for hours, about everything from growing up in small towns to living our dreams. Rain was working at *ACAL Magazine* then and taking sewing classes on Saturdays. I had just completed the academy and was in the process of applying to the FBI.

"Isn't that supposed to be top secret information? Sounds dangerous."

"I think once I'm hired, I have to go around telling people I work for UPS, or some job that no one cares to have further details about."

"Interesting. Does that mean you aren't going to be around a lot?"

"Did we already make it past our first date and our second year of dating?" I asked jokingly.

"Um, well . . . no" Rain said, trying not to sound defeated. She nervously began to pick at invisible lint on her pants.

Her embarrassment was obvious, from the way her cheeks flushed to the intense blinking every time our eyes met. At the academy, I'd learned to read body language better than verbal cues. That profiler training was definitely paying off.

"I'm just asking." Snatched by awkwardness, Rain's response was dry. I could tell that all the saliva had left her mouth by the way she kept swallowing. Though she was a very beautiful woman, I could tell she found it hard to talk to men, in particular attractive ones like me.

"I'm only giving you a hard time. That's a valid question. I will be away for a few months for training, but I don't want to be an agent—just the computer nerd with a corner office. You know, like Garcia on *Criminal Minds*. Minus the obnoxious clothing and blond hair."

Rain laughed. "I can only imagine you in a polyester dress and chili pepper earrings."

Finding out that we had so much in common, especially *Criminal Minds*, seemed to have made her feel a little more comfortable.

"So, hopefully you get used to seeing me every day." I flashed a smile, exposing the crescent-shaped dimple on my left cheek.

Rain's cheeks turned red, I wasn't sure whether from intrigue or timidity. I touched her hand, which made her jump. Not in an "Eww, boys are gross" way; I felt a shock go straight to my heart. It was more than static electricity. It was almost a burning pain.

Rain placed her nervous, shaking hands in her lap. "Did you feel that?" she asked.

"Sorry. I didn't mean to touch you. I'm still working on that whole personal bubble thing women have."

I didn't want to risk mentioning the shock I felt. I didn't want to come off as corny, saying we had an instant connection or something—even though we literally did, I guess. At some point we'd need to discuss what had just happened.

"It's fine. I just haven't—" Rain's cheeks became flushed again. As if to get through the awkward moment, she blurted out "I guess you confirmed that we've made it past the first date." We both laughed.

Time continued to fly by. As joggers changed, and new football teams formed on the grass in front of us, and tiny petals began to fall from the tree, I discovered that Rain was an avid reader and writer. Her dream was to be the next Anna Wintour, and her passion was designing gowns. There's nothing more attractive than a small-town girl, with big-city dreams. She told me how she'd finished undergrad in just three years by going to school year-round.

"How do you find time for dating?"

"I don't—well, I try, I just haven't found that special someone yet."

I couldn't believe this stunning woman was single. What are the chances? I wondered. To avoid sounding cheesy by telling her what I was thinking, I just coolly said, "I see," flashing a smile.

Two years of braces as a teen had left me with what I call the twenty-six lady killers. I could almost count the seconds to the moment a woman was captivated.

Rain was harder to read. Through the blushing and flirty laughter, I still couldn't tell if she was into me or just being nice. So rather than spoil a good moment, I chose to end it. I preferred to save the rest for our first date. Or maybe our lifetime together.

After exchanging phone numbers, we stood up and gave one another an awkward hug. I got an eerie feeling of déjà vu. Everything felt familiar, as if our meeting had happened before. But unless we'd been in a terrible accident and lost our memory, it couldn't have.

When I turned to wave goodbye for the third time, Rain was still smiling and waving back. That feeling football players have when scoring a touchdown was the only way I could think of to describe the moment. I didn't want to humiliate myself by doing an obnoxious dance, though, so I just did the Michael Jordan one-fist-in-the-air jump.

I could still smell his cologne on my skin. Exhaling, I felt a little dizzy and realized I had been holding my breath the entire time. Oh, and that spark! I wondered if he felt it too.

I watched Erick walk all the way to the end of the trail, until I could no longer make out more than a shadow. But I did catch a glimpse of him jumping up in the air, Michael Jordan style. I'll be sure to bring it up when I see him again.

If someone asked me for the definition of love, I would simply say "the feeling of forever butterflies." I felt more than a flutter, but a feeling of genuine excitement when I met Erick. I'd never looked forward to hearing from someone again so soon.

Buzz—buzz—buzz. I looked down at my phone. It was a text from an unsaved number:

> "I don't want to come off as desperate, but I really enjoyed our conversation. How about we continue over dinner tonight?"

I quickly saved the number under *Erick* with a heart. Then I smiled, exhaled, and replied:

> You took the words right out of my mouth. I'll be ready at 8. Meet me at the Pier."

Then I gathered my pen and notebook and took off toward my apartment to get ready.

We spent the next 305 days together. The other sixty days we were apart due to Erick's obligation to the academy. One year after our chance encounter at Sibley Park, we were engaged. Six months later, I married the man of my dreams.

12

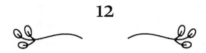

Our wedding day was like a scene out of your favorite fairytale. Rain glued cherry blossom petals to Styrofoam balls and attached them to crystal candelabras. We had a wedding planner, but Rain wanted to add lots of personal touches to our big day. We got married under the cherry blossom tree where we first met.

The wedding was perfect in everyone's eyes, except for our parents. Lily and Pop were nervous wrecks, and I wasn't sure if my family would even show up. Don't get me wrong, there's no bad blood between our families, but neither side was gung-ho about our nuptials. We were one big family while we were dating, but once we got engaged, my family did everything they could to break us up. Fortunately for us, our love only grew stronger. My mother told me she was worried about my wellbeing, which is bizarre. The Novas are almost too perfect. They don't even have anything as small as a speeding ticket or jaywalking on their records.

As my palms began to sweat, and just before my best man Chris decided to draft Poppy for backup, in walked my parents.

"You look handsome, son."

"I thought you two weren't going to make it."

"We wouldn't miss our only son's wedding. Besides, you're marrying a very wonderful woman."

I would know, since I ran multiple background checks at the office. An FBI agent needs to be extra vigilant about relationships.

Only my stepdad had spoken. My mother's been very emotional lately, and she couldn't manage to form any words, only tears. But I could tell she was happy for me. Her eyes were very kind.

It was funny that any of this was happening after they spent so much time trying to tear Rain and me apart.

"In spite of being at the venue, dressed, and ready to see my bride, I don't think I could have gone through the ceremony without you two." We embraced in a huddle.

"Stop that crying, or Erick is going to mess up his makeup!" My mother jokingly exclaimed. Everyone laughed, including Chris, who was trying to remain lowkey during the family meeting.

"Excuse me for a second—here, son, you'll need this." My stepdad poured all the groomsmen a celebratory drink. I downed the brown liquor and left the suite to get some air.

I needed some time alone to digest everything that had just taken place. I turned down the marble hallway. Just before exiting to the terrace, I overheard Lily telling Pop that she hoped Rain's tears of joy wouldn't cause any problems during the ceremony.

What kind of mother would expect her daughter not to be emotional on her big day? Either they just killed my best man, or the good luck shot had been stronger than I thought. Or maybe Lily had just lost her mind.

Maybe she was worried about how my family would perceive Rain's emotions. She already wasn't taking my last name, due to a strict family tradition. And we'd agreed that if we had children, my surname would be their middle name.

My in-law's conversation was bizarre, but it felt weirder when I realized that I had never actually seen Rain cry. Aren't all women emotional? I took credit for her happiness, and I was proud I'd never made her cry, but she hadn't even cried during *P.S. I Love You.* Even I shed a few allergy tears during that movie.

Sometimes Rain would joke, "I have blocked tear ducts." But I guess I'd just convinced myself that she was the happiest woman on the planet.

I do believe Rain made me a better man by being so positive, and I couldn't wait to spend forever with her, and even have children together—something we rarely discuss. I can only imagine how beautiful a child of ours would be.

On the day I proposed, she kept pinching her arm. I thought it was just nerves. Or perhaps she was pinching herself to make sure she wasn't dreaming. Do people actually do that? I thought it was just a figure of speech.

Immediately my mind started replaying the past 847 days. I'd seen tears well up in Rain's eyes, but she'd never once let them stream down her face. And every time, the sky would grow dark and then return to sunshine, just like that, within seconds. The only time this bizarre weather occurred was when I was near Rain. Anastasia is known for its great weather. That's the main reason people move here.

I shared everything with this woman, but realizing that I had never seen her cry disturbed my soul. *We* shared everything, or so I thought.

Lily and Pop continued to whisper on the other side of the wall, and I finally found the courage to speak up. I cleared my throat. "Ma—Pop—is Rain OK?"

Pop just stood back in shock. He should have seen this coming, though. Ma Lily headed toward the bridal suite without responding.

Rain was getting ready with Aster, Iris, Azalea, and Suri when Lily entered the suite, her hands trembling.

They'd all grown up together, starting when their parents had named them all after wonders of nature. The four bridesmaids wore beautiful floor-length, ocean-blue silk and lace dresses, each bodice matching its wearer's personality. Aster was the most conservative of the group, so her bodice gathered beautifully into a high collar. Iris was the opposite, and her dress was backless. Azalea wore a one-shoulder dress befitting her indecisiveness. And Suri, Rain's best friend, was a free spirit and had chosen a strapless gown. She hated feeling restricted by anything.

Rain worked tirelessly on her bridal party's gowns. Lily had helped with the alterations and intricate hand beading. She'd joked about using superpowers to help her sew—her old hands were growing tired. Every weekend Rain stopped by; she'd be working tirelessly in her sewing room. She never allowed Rain to help her. She wanted to present the dresses as a gift to her daughter. Rain was a writer, but her heart was in designing gowns. Her wedding day would be the world's first vision of her new passion.

"Baby, you look beautiful! All of you are stunning," Lily said.

As Rain turned to thank her mother, she noticed the sadness in her eyes, and before Lily could speak, Rain said, "Take me to him!"

The room grew quiet. The bridesmaids jumped up to help Rain with her dress, but she just held up a hand. "Excuse me, ladies."

Pop walked me back to the groom's suite, cupping my shoulder as reassurance that everything was OK.

Back in the room, lost in my thoughts, I didn't notice Rain entering until she was standing behind me. If it weren't for the beveled floor mirror in front of me, I would never have noticed at all. She was already beautiful, and seeing my future wife in her wedding dress, my heart nearly stopped. Everyone else must have felt the same way, because all seven of their mouths hung open. I saw Chris nudge Mike, both of their eyes wide, mouthing "Wow." Thank God I was already sitting, or I would have fallen on my face.

The thin lace hugged her body with perfection. The tiny beads Lily had added last night danced like diamonds in the light. Rain wore little makeup in general, but today she had a makeup artist who had made my future wife even more beautiful than I could have imagined. Tiny sparkles, like glitter to the naked eye but really specks of Nova magic, danced around her eyelids. I could feel the intensity of whatever she was about to say.

"I'm not supposed to see you. Isn't it bad luck?" I asked.

Lily entered the room behind Rain and carefully closed the heavy cherrywood door so no one in the hallway could hear their conversation, and she answered first. "Not as bad as what we have to tell you. Everyone except the Brentons, please excuse us."

The groomsmen left a bit reluctantly, each patting me on the shoulder on the way out. They spotted the bridesmaids sneaking into the hallway to eavesdrop and escorted them to the bridal suite around the corner.

Every possible bad thought entered my mind. My heart began to race. Rain must have sensed something was wrong because she ran to me, grabbed my hand, and held it to her heart. The palpitations stopped at once and I was able to focus on her. Through my tears and confusion, I said "Tell me."

My voice cracked. In that moment, I wasn't trying to be strong, I wasn't trying to hold it together. I just prayed that whatever she had to tell me wouldn't break my heart.

Rain was still holding my hand to her heart when Ma Lily spoke the words that no man wants to hear on his wedding day.

"You can't marry our daughter."

My mother mumbled her agreement. Dad pulled up two chairs so they could both sit beside me. However, I could no longer be quiet. I jumped up, not in a threatening manner but because it was easier to grab Rain and run away.

"Ma! Don't do this! I love her!"

I could feel myself growing angry, but with my hand still touching my fiancés heart, I calmed down, strangely. If Rain wanted to marry me, what could our parents possibly need to tell me at a time like this? It seemed like everyone was in on a secret except me.

"Is this some sort of twisted joke?"

Ma Lily finally gathered the courage to let go of doorknob and walk toward the group. Pop must have felt some relief, because he became unstuck and walked closer too, joining my parents. Rain, still holding my left hand, tugged at my arm with her other hand so I would sit down. I placed my left hand in her lap.

Poised as any queen, Ma Lily spoke. "We need to explain something to you. You need to listen with your heart and not try to make sense of it. Poppy and I love you like our own son, which is why this is so hard for us."

I could feel my heart breaking and all the pieces piercing through my chest and falling to the floor. With my free hand, I clenched my fist. I wished that someone had prepared me for whatever I was going to hear next. Even if they had, though, I still wouldn't have been ready. I would later learn that Lily chose this moment to start speaking after hearing my thoughts.

"I know you've wondered why Rain never gets emotional—I mean, why you've never seen her cry. I'm sure you've questioned a lot before today but have been afraid to ask."

"Mom, don't," Rain said, frightened.

"It's OK, baby. The Brentons know a little about what's going on. We aren't breaking any rules by letting them know. Poppy received confirmation that our secret will remain safe." Ma Lily nodded reassuringly to her daughter, then continued. "When I'm around you, I can hear your thoughts. You've wondered why we've been so adamant about you two not marrying."

"Hear my thoughts? How do you know I've questioned that?"

"I have the power—the gift of reading thoughts. Don't worry, son, in my old age I can block out what I don't want to hear."

I was confused and frightened, but I gestured for her to continue. We were set to walk down the aisle in forty minutes. That is, if what they had to tell me didn't send me packing.

"Rain doesn't cry because strange things happen when she does. We taught her at a young age how to control her emotions so she can live a somewhat normal life. Before today, we were ecstatic for you to marry her. But then Poppy had a vision. I will explain it in a moment—yes, honey, Poppy can see the future."

Pop began to speak. "Our daughter has the power to alter the weather with her tears. The women in Lily's family develop powers when they reach maturity."

Lily interjected, sounding as if she had rehearsed her words carefully. "We Novas have to be careful who we love."

Next to me, Rain held her breath.

"Love conquers all, but it also takes a lot of energy. You must be careful who you share your energy with. Otherwise it can drain so much from you that you're left empty or shattered. But with the right person, it can fill you up, creating bliss. Love is its own superpower. Any man a Nova marries will develop powers as well, but only after conceiving a female child. The Novas are superhuman."

Laughing, because I feel crazy hearing this story, I ask "So you're telling me you don't want me to marry Rain because of the power I will develop? Or because you're afraid I'll make her unhappy and cause a natural disaster?"

"Both," my mother, Ma Lily, and Pop answered in unison.

I could tell this was Rain's first-time hearing this. She looked just as stunned as I felt. The craziest part was that my parents were aware of it before she and I was. "Our love hasn't changed the weather so far," she said. "Erick only makes me happy. And the only thing you ever told me was that I would have powers. You never said they could affect anyone else if I learned to control them. I spent most of my life learning to control my tears by showing any other emotion, only for you to tell me this—on my wedding day!"

A loud clap of thunder shook the building. Outside the window, I saw some petals from the cherry blossoms fall to the ground.

The whole room shook, and Suri jumped.

Though Rain had told her best friend about the Novas secret during a night of partying in college, growing up Suri always had a sneaking suspicion. She'd known Rain since birth, and they were just a few weeks apart in age. Now, not wanting to scare anyone more than the thunder already had, nor to reveal Rain's secret, Suri stood in front of the bridal suite door so the wedding party couldn't leave.

This wasn't the way Rain would want her secret revealed, she knew. Especially since the two of them would need to discuss everything first. Besides, Iris had a big mouth, and she would kill to be the first journalist to break news like this. There were already whispers around Anastasia, even though no one dared to ask questions.

My mother gasped, and my dad shifted in his seat, trying not to appear frightened.

"Son, my vision showed that you will die if you and my daughter have a child together." For the first time since Rain was born, Pop began to cry.

My mother clutched at her heart as he continued.

"Your power will be that you love my daughter and your child so much that your heart explodes."

"How is that a superpower? Sounds more like you're foreseeing my future health problems!"

I lost my biological father when I was very young. My mother told me that his heart had given out because of all the love he had for everyone. Superpowers weren't prevalent in the Brenton family; all this was hard for me to accept.

My mother, like Rain, is a writer. She's written many science fiction novels, so her imagination is a little bizarre. But I love her, so I accepted anything she said, even if it sounded like something from one of her novels. I knew my dad had actually died from a heart attack. People die of heart attacks every day, I understood, and she was just making his death a little gentler on my young ears. But now I thought maybe there was more to the Brenton family story than I'd had time to figure out.

"Your power is in the way you love. If you have a son first, you will be fine, but if you have a daughter, there is a chance you will die. There is also a possibility that the child will die, though it could happen during delivery or years later," Ma Lily said.

Rain and I never discussed having kids. I guess we've spent every second just wanting to be around one another, forgetting a topic more important than interests and religion.

"We don't have to have kids. We can adopt."

"This type of power has only appeared one other time in Nova history. It happened with Lily's great-grandparents. No one ever spoke of it, but Lily came across a short story in The *Nova Book of Magic*, which she hasn't seen since Rain was a teenager."

Angrily, I yelled "That's called life, Pop!"

I immediately apologized for raising my voice. I had a lot of respect for the old man.

Rain started to cry. She could no longer hold in her pain. Her arms were bright red from all the pinching. And then Lily opened the curtains, revealing the rain drops that were falling in sync with her tears: "Look!"

For the second time today, everyone looked stunned.

"It all makes sense," Rain said crying.

Through the thin wall, Suri overheard Lily. She told Azalea to open the curtains so the wedding party could see what was going on outside. Another storm was brewing. Good thing there weren't many decorations, or the wedding would be ruined.

"Rain is good luck for a wedding," Suri said awkwardly.

"If superstitions are true, Rain and Erick are going to be the luckiest couple on earth. This is one hell of a storm," Mike laughed.

"Remember the day we met?"

I nodded because I knew what Rain was going to say next.

In unison, we said, "The spark!"

Our parents looked stunned, yet curious.

"I was afraid to say anything. It would have sounded cheesy, but I felt a shock that went straight to my heart."

"Me too," Rain said.

"Erick is a Brenton," my mother interrupted. "Love is like a flame. Brenton means flame."

We all looked at one another, confused.

"At the end of our life, it runs out of fuel. Our core becomes so heavy that it can't withstand gravity, and ultimately it explodes. When the two worlds collide, bad things can happen." The Brenton's aren't superhuman—I think. But mom is very spiritual and believes in things that most people don't; yet she believes in science more than anything.

"If I believe you," I said, "how does this affect me?"

"Son, you can't marry her. This is why I fought so hard for you to leave her alone. The rumors about this family are true!"

"If Rain marries someone else, could the same thing happen?"

"Something would happen, but we can't be sure what until Poppy has a vision," Ma Lily answered.

"Is this some kind of sick modern-day Romeo-and-Juliet joke? I already told Rain she doesn't have to take my last name. But now this? I will do anything to be this woman. I more than love her."

"Listen to me, son. There is such a thing as loving someone too much." Now Lily was crying.

Rain could no longer fight back her tears and almost on que, the rain started again. It wasn't a light drizzle, but huge drops fell from the sky, with no clouds in site.

Looking into my fiancée's eyes, I realized I couldn't live without her. The power of love doesn't compare to the feeling I would have not being with Rain. Love conquers all. It can take so much from a person that they're left with only emptiness or a broken heart, but it can also fill them up, creating a superpower. I felt more than powerful when we were together.

Crying, I got on my knees in front of the Novas and my parents and professed my love for all of them, promising to be around for as long as they would have me.

"We will hope and pray for the best. We love you two."

"Let's just hope history doesn't repeat itself," Ma Lily whispered.

Everyone hugged. My parents finally gave their blessing.

"I don't think we would have been able to stop them. Look at the way he looks at her," my mom said.

I delicately dried Rain's tears with my index finger, and the storm started to clear.

"I have to fix my makeup before you rethink this whole marriage," she laughed, and she gathered the bottom of her dress and hurried out of the room. But before she reached the door, she stopped and turned to say, "I love you."

"Forever and always."

"Let's get married, Mr. Brenton." Rain smirked and turned back to the door. She was almost in a full sprint as she made her way back to the bridal suite to freshen up.

Everything else about our wedding day was perfect. Rain walked down the aisle toward me, and even though I'd seen her just an hour before, she looked even more beautiful saying, "I do."

I kept tickling her so she wouldn't cry. I cried enough for the both us anyway.

I closed my eyes and entered the place where I see Daddy every night. He was standing by my closet when I opened them again. I sat up, and he motioned for me to follow him into the closet. That meant we were going into my treehouse.

I grabbed his hand, and he squeezed my fingers as a way of saying hello. The door from my closet to the treehouse creaked. I guess I hadn't used that entrance as much. Inside, Daddy pulled out the cherrywood chair from underneath the round table that Poppy had made.

"Why are we here, Daddy?"

"I just wanted to meet you somewhere else. That's all, Blossom."

"I have so much to tell you, Daddy."

He turned away. "I know, Blossom. You look so beautiful. More beautiful than the last time I saw you."

Attempting to lighten the mood, he asked how school was going, and about Mom, Poppy, and Granny Lily. I answered all his questions, even telling him how much Mom missed him.

"Daddy, I know we don't have much time, but I wanted to tell you about my powers."

"You've gotten really good at controlling your hair, I see. I miss your wild curls."

I hadn't noticed but, my braid had unraveled itself, each of the three strands uncoiling in a different direction. One strand grabbed the teacups from the center of the table, another lifted the teapot, and the last strand, pulling my head somewhat to the left, was stretching toward my bookshelf. I knew it was going for the *Nova Book of Magic*.

"Have a seat, Daddy."

"Um, B, how long has this tea been here?" Daddy winked.

"I never actually put tea in the pot. But this is my dream, and anything we want to appear in the cup, will."

"Hm. Well, can you make sure my tea has a double shot of Jack Daniels? I haven't had one of those in years. Just make sure that your little cup only has tea, sunshine."

"Aw, man! I was hoping you would let me have soda."

"Of course! Just don't mix it with a grown-up drink." Daddy flashed a smile with his blinding white, perfect teeth.

As my hair prepared our drinks, Daddy took a pen and paper from my bookshelf. "Tell me about your powers. I want to write them down so I won't forget, and then maybe I can help you with them."

My eyes opened wide with excitement. I hadn't spent much time thinking about my powers, beyond learning to control them. My hands tightened on my white porcelain teacup full of Sprite. The bubbles popped up, hitting my top lip.

I'd never seen Daddy's handwriting before. It was a lot better than Mom's. It kind of looked like my writing.

Powers
1. Talk to and heal animals

"After discovering my first power, Mom and I went to Sibley Park and dug up the *Nova Book of Magic* so I could learn how to control it. A while back she revealed that she tore out some of the pages, but that's all I heard. My ears stopped working."

Daddy looked confused. And like Poppy says, the wheels started turning in my head. "You know how the cherry blossom tree in Sibley Park stays in bloom all year long?"

"Yeah . . ."

"What if it stays in bloom because of the buried pages? What if they work like seeds of some sort?"

Daddy set the pen down on the paper. "Your mom told me why she buried those pages."

Since I didn't hear the explanation from Mom, I was hoping Daddy would tell me, but he didn't. He just cleared his throat, picked up the pen again, and continued writing. I could see pain in his eyes. Maybe it was anger. He had his jaw clenched and was holding the pen so tight the veins in his hand popped out more than usual.

"Are you OK, Daddy?"

"I'm fine." He didn't look up from the paper.

2. Change flowers
3. Hair

I explained the story of washing my face and noticing the enormous pimple between my eyes, and how after Mom took a picture of me, she dropped her phone and it shattered.

"Can you bring the photos with you tomorrow?"

"I don't know. They're on Mom's phone. Wait, do I look different to you?"

"You do. I just didn't want to say anything. I know this whole power thing has been hard for you, but you are absolutely gorgeous, Blossom. Tell Poppy it's time to bring out the shotgun." Daddy's face was serious. "I know you're going to middle school soon, and boys are going to start noticing you. Promise me you will not have a boyfriend until you're twenty-five."

"Dad! I don't even like boys. Eww! Some of them smell."

"Well, good. Remember, little boys grow up to be stinky men." He laughed.

"You don't smell bad, Daddy. Neither does Poppy."

"We are the exception. We are Novas."

I placed my head in my hands. Boys were the last thing on my mind. I can't even control my ten-year-old life. I have no time to focus on anything else.

"We don't have much time, let's try to get this finished." Daddy scribbled down my fourth power.

4. Beauty

Then he wrote down the gifts that he had given me before each change.

Gifts
Rosebuds
No gift
Rope
Jeweled mirror

"Did I get them all, beautiful?"

"Yes, Daddy. Let's try to figure out what the powers mean and where they came from."

"We already know that the Dream Keeper gives me the gifts, and each signifies a new power and a body change." Next to the list of gifts, he wrote the meanings.

Rosebuds = Breast buds
No gift? = Change wildflowers into other flowers
Rope = Strength in hair
Jeweled mirror = With every pimple, Blossom becomes more beautiful

He paused. "I don't think last one is really a power."

"How else can we explain it?"

"True. We do know that with every change of your body, I present you with a gift. I think they are clues to your powers."

"Daddy, you're a genius! Why didn't I think of that sooner?"

"You are just a kid, Blossom, and I am—was—an FBI agent. It was my job to figure out things like this."

"But I didn't get a gift before I discovered my flower-changing power."

"Hmmm. Did you experience any other changes in your body?"

"Daddy!" I felt my cheeks burn with embarrassment. But I thought about it for a minute, and I realized something had changed. But I didn't want to tell him about it. I guess from the look on my face, he could tell that I was uncomfortable.

"Blossom, you have to tell me. I know it may be weird and uncomfortable. But believe me, I've heard it all."

I shuffled my feet under the table, still not making eye contact. "Um, well . . . when I took a bath . . . there was some hair down there. A lot more than before."

"Oh, ok. Got it. Well, that is definitely a change. I wondered why the Dream Keeper didn't have a gift for you."

"Well, Dad—Daddy—I sort of used Mom's shaver to cut it off." My face blazed with embarrassment.

"Blossom!"

Daddy lowered his tone. He could tell I was a mess of emotions and didn't want to make things worse. So, he walked over to me and laid his hands on my shoulders.

"Look at me. Blossom, I'm pretty sure your mom doesn't want you to shave yet."

I nodded. "She said I can shave when I turn twelve. But she lets me shave my armpits and legs, since I got teased at school."

"Teased? We'll talk about that later. Blossom you have to tell your mom."

"I know, Daddy."

"Is there anything else you need to tell me?"

"Yesterday, when I got my new power, Mom took a picture of me but then dropped her phone."

"You said that. And?"

"Mom said you were in the picture with me."

Daddy looked confused. "I can't haunt you, Blossom. When I died, I asked whomever it is that you see in the white light to let me move on. I didn't want to make life harder for you, by randomly knocking things over to make my presence known, or whatever ghosts do."

Still confused, I had no response. I just looked at my toes, which were long overdue for painting.

"Maybe your mom just imagined it."

"Yeah, maybe."

Daddy tore off a small corner of paper from our list and scribbled something on it. He folded it into a tiny triangle and placed it in my hand.

"Give this to your mom when you wake up. If you try to read it before giving it to her, the words will disappear."

I had enough energy to just nod my head.

Daddy never brought me anything for Mom in my dreams. I hope that I can bring it back from the dream realm. I can't wait to see her expression.

Daddy folded up the list of my powers and tucked it inside the *Nova Book of Magic*.

"Do you have a gift for me tonight?" I hope he doesn't.

"Actually, not tonight, Blossom. All I know is that you will wake up feeling different."

"Will I have to miss school?"

"I don't know." Daddy looked away.

I guess I'll get a gift tomorrow. I felt my stomach clench. I wish I didn't have powers. They're pretty cool, but what fun is it if I can't even show my friends?

The sun hadn't even had a chance to turn the backs of my eyelids orange when my body began to shake.

"Blossom, wake up."

I opened my eyes. My mom was standing over me. "How did you end up in here?"

"In where?"

My back hurt a little. I pushed myself up with the palms of my hands and looked around. I was still in my treehouse.

"Daddy told me to follow him in here to talk. When I wake up, I'm always back in my bed."

"You'll have to tell me what happened later. You have to get up or you're going to be late for school."

I held out my right hand. It still held the letter that Daddy wrote to Mom. She asked what it was for, but I didn't know, so I just shrugged. My body ached from lying on the floor. The only thing on my mind was taking a shower.

While Blossom was upstairs getting ready, I sliced some fruit in the kitchen so that she'd at least have something to eat on the way to school. I saw a squirrel scurrying up the tree toward the treehouse. I hoped it didn't need help because I didn't want Blossom to be late.

I spoke to Poppy about the picture on Blossom's phone. He'd had no visions, and he insisted that it was all my imagination. And even when I powered on my old phone, the picture just was of Blossom. A very beautiful Blossom. Maybe I'm losing my mind.

I forgot about the letter she handed me until I was clearing off the countertop and almost swept it into the trashcan. The folded note was surrounded by those golden sparkles that appear when Blossom uses her powers. I could tell that Erick had torn the page from one of Blossom's dream journals, because the back of the note was covered with my own handwriting. I'm glad it was the very last page of the journal, because it would've been hard for me to read a letter on top of my own writing.

Carefully opening the delicate beige sheet that was folded into a triangle, I had an overwhelming feeling of happiness. I hadn't received anything from Erick in the dream realm, and I feared the note would have become blank when Blossom woke up. But it was covered in Erick's neat handwriting.

I skimmed to the bottom. I could tell he was in rush because he signed the letter

Forever and Always,
Your Hub E (I thought this was kinda cute. I miss you dearly)

When Erick was alive, he would send me letters every week, because he knew I loved to read. He even proposed in a letter. And he would always end his letters with, "your husband," as if I would forget. It was his mission to make me laugh. Now at a time when I found it hard to do just that, he signed the letter "Hub E" instead of hubby. How cute!

Not having time to sulk, I figured I should read the note right now. Blossom would be running down the stairs any minute. On a slow day, it takes her thirty minutes from start to finish, so I have about two minutes before I hear her rubber soles screeching across our wood floors.

As I read the note in my head, I imagined Erick reading it to me aloud:

Rain,

I hope this letter makes it to you. I met with Blossom and we figured out her powers and how they correlate to the gifts. She's watching me, so I can't include everything in the letter, but I placed the list in the front cover of the Nova Book of Magic. Please read it—if you can, while B is at school.

Don't yell at B or cry, but she informed me that she's been growing hair in all the places we don't want to imagine. That explains why she gained the wildflower power without me presenting a gift to her first. B shaved, which confused the Dream

Keeper. Please make sure she feels comfortable enough to tell you EVERYTHING about her changes.

If you can read this, I wish I'd thought to write you notes sooner. I just don't want to complicate things where I am, or to ruin seeing Blossom every night. Hopefully her dreams never end.

I'm pretty sure I've been in limbo for all these years. I never see any familiar faces. I haven't met God or any of the people in the Bible. There are no pearly gates anywhere. I just sit in a house with everything I dreamed of having, but I feel empty. There's no you or Blossom.

The sun is coming up. I'll write you soon. Talk to Blossom.

Forever and Always,

Your Hub E (I thought this was kinda cute. I miss you dearly)

P.S. DON'T DIG UP THE MISSING PAGES

I held the letter to my heart. The shock I felt on the day I met Erick still stings my chest. I wanted to go back to retrieve the missing pages, for Blossom's sake, but maybe Erick was right. Maybe digging the pages up would do more harm.

I refolded the note, careful to not tear the thin paper, and placed it in the tiny pocket inside of my purse. Before I could look up, I heard the patter of Blossom's bare feet, not the squeal of her sneakers.

"Mom, I can explain."

She must have seen the disappointment in my face. "Why aren't you dressed? You have to be at school in fifteen minutes." Remembering Erick's note, I was cautious about my tone.

"I know, Mom. A squirrel—Roger was throwing acorns at my window when I got out of the shower. He told me that Mr. Little, the sweet old man who lives near the pier—his dog has fallen ill, and I need to go save him now."

"You have to go to school, Blossom. How are you supposed to get on Mr. Little's boat and heal his dog without him noticing?"

"That's what took so long. Roger helped me devise a plan. I'll need both of your help. He'll pretend to attack you, and you'll cry—I'll explain the rest in the car. I need to finish getting dressed."

All I could do was obey. I know that she's the one person who can help, even if that means being a little late to school.

The car ride to Mr. Little's boat was awkward. Mom let me sit in the front seat because Roger the squirrel was in the trunk, and she was afraid he would get nervous and bite me, and then I'd get rabies. She still hasn't gotten used to me being an animal healer. I can easily cure any condition with just my fingertips.

I wished the car ride were shorter so that Mom wouldn't have time to ask if I'd started shaving down there again. That letter Daddy gave me must have told her everything. I felt betrayed, but like Mom says, we're a team, and he had no choice. I might have screwed up my powers by getting rid of the hair on my body.

"Mom, I know it was wrong, but I watched YouTube, and I didn't cut myself. I even used a new razor."

"I understand, but you should have come to me."

"I didn't think about it—my powers, I mean. I noticed you don't have hair anywhere, and I didn't think that I should either."

Mom smacked herself on the forehead with her palm, the way she always does when she has an *aha* moment. "OMG! That makes so much sense. I mean—I did tell you what to expect, but in all the madness I didn't pay attention. We could've talked about it. Just know that you cannot shave again until you're at least twelve."

"Twelve! Do you know how much hair is on my body? It literally looked like I shaved all the hair off my head into the bathtub."

Mom laughed. "Yes. You must be careful about shaving. Especially your vag—twinker. We're still calling it a twinker, right? There are all sorts of things you have to consider, like hygiene, bacteria, infections—let's just say it's hard being a woman—a young lady."

"Tell me about it! And yes, I still call the v-word a twinker."

"Well, next time it starts growing—a lot—just
let me know. I am your mom. I'm here to help you,
even in times that are embarrassing. I want you to
be comfortable enough to talk to me about anything.
And I mean *anything*, Blossom."

"OK."

"Lighten up, B. You're not in trouble. Besides,
you need to put your game face on. We're almost
at the pier."

13

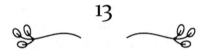

I didn't get much sleep last night. I tossed and turned so much that Daddy couldn't enter my dreams. When I opened one eye to check the time, the glare of the red numbers burned 5:30 into my retina. There was still an hour before my alarm went off.

My body ached. Sitting up, I stretched as tall as I could. Looking in the mirror across from my bed, I didn't need to put on my glasses to see that my hair was a curly mess. Between the strong winds and the waves crashing onto Mr. Little's boat, it had morphed into a nest. I was way too tired to wash my hair before school, so I decided to use my power. I massaged my scalp with my fingers, and my hair slowly began to untangle. Strand by strand, my curls uncoiled and recoiled into neat French braids on the sides of my head. Once the second blue ribbon tied itself into a bow, I stood up to stretch once more. Not wanting to face another day like yesterday, I opened my journal.

Yesterday, I wasn't able to save Mr. Little's dog. I know he was old, and I'm not God, but why give me the power to heal if I can't?

My tears soaked the page. I closed my journal and threw it so hard against the wall that the paint chipped. I was afraid the thud would wake Mom, so

I sat in silence awaiting the patter of her bare feet on the hardwood floor. But Mom must have been just as tired, because she never came to my room, or even let out a sigh like she does when she's annoyed.

"What's the point of my power?" I yelled, covering my mouth to drown my screams.

There was a light tap at my window. The wind was blowing, so it was probably a tree branch. I kept crying, but the tapping repeated. Slowly turning to the window, I saw Roger the squirrel waving his tiny paws. I gently opened the window and told Roger never to return to my house. I couldn't help him or any others. Before he could respond, I slammed the window shut and closed the blue sequined curtain. On my way to the shower, I unplugged my alarm clock and slammed the bathroom door.

The car ride to school was silent. Mom tried to talk to me about yesterday, but I put on my headphones and cranked the sound up to block out my thoughts. When we pulled up to the curb, I mumbled, "I love you too," not knowing if she'd even said anything.

Em was the first person to greet me in the hallway. I just waved. She looked pained by my response, but I had nothing in me to be nice. Mr. Little's dog had died in my arms, and these stupid fingers of mine couldn't even offer it any comfort.

14

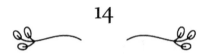

Like most kids, I like to run around the house naked, but the more my body changes, the more self-conscious I'm becoming. Even though it's just Mom and me, I still find it funny when I run past her and she says, "Girl, you need to put some clothes on—at least a bra and some underwear."

This morning was no different. I got out of the shower and was making a beeline to my bedroom to grab underwear when I bumped into mom.

"B, no running in the house. Did you forget that you're clumsy?"

"No, Mom, I just wanted to make it to my room before you yelled at me to put some clothes on."

"Oh, honey, you know I don't mind. I just want you to get in the habit of wearing clothes in case we have company."

I made it my room to put on the clothes my mom had picked out. I could see from the doorway those hideous frilly orange shorts that I hate. I've tried to throw them away many times, but Mom has always snuck them back into my drawer.

I picked out something else to wear. I replaced those awful shorts with some dark, skinny jeans. I found a plain white t-shirt, but since growing boobs, I felt more comfortable in sweatshirts. Poppy bought me a red Nike sweatshirt last week, and I pulled that over my head. Before leaving my room, I stopped in front of my bejeweled mirror. There were two larger-than-usual lumps on my chest. I'd just gotten used to the boobs I had; there was no way I could deal with bigger ones.

"Mom come now! My chest is swollen!"

Mom burst into my room and saw me standing in front of the mirror unclothed, examining my body. The clothes I had so excitedly put on were now scattered on my floor.

"Did something bite you, honey? Does it itch or burn?" asked Mom as she examined my body, before realizing what swollen parts I was referring to.

"Those mosquitoes bit me when I was playing superhero in Granny Lily's garden. Can we put some bug repellent on the bites, so my friends won't mistake them for bigger boobs?"

My mom couldn't control her laughter. "Blossom, those two swollen things are your breasts. They're just bigger."

This was no laughing matter, and Mom realized I was serious. We looked at one another, and then with wide eyes, we both yelled "Oh no!"

I didn't want another cake for my birthday. I think my mom got more satisfaction from having cakes made than I got from eating them. I'm more of a cookies and ice cream kind of kid. This year, Sweet Treats made me a dozen double chocolate chip cookies.

Mom placed one candle in the middle of each cookie. I gave the extra cookie to Poppy. Even though he claims to hate chocolate, I saw him sneak a few of my brownies last week.

I inhaled and held my breath for ten seconds. For every second, I made a wish that my superpowers would go away. After the tenth, I exhaled. The candles went out, and I am now eleven years old.

It's that time again—the dreaded trip to the mall. Not for clothes, but for new, bigger bras. This time was also a little different because Granny Lily decided to come with us. I was already annoyed by the reason we were at the mall, but Granny Lily hurt her knee a few weeks ago while running from her neighbor's greyhound, and she was walking extremely slow. Because I'm not allowed to go out of Mom's sight, I had to walk slower than dirt.

Sometimes I walked ahead and waited on a bench until Mom and Granny got closer. Granny Lily could tell I was annoyed and told us to go ahead, which made me feel bad. My hormones were starting to affect my moods, and everyone noticed. The only person who didn't seem to get on my nerves was

Poppy. Unfortunately, bra shopping is not either of our thing, so he had stayed home.

"Go ahead with your mom. I'll be here when you get back." Granny Lily patted my knee.

"I'm sorry, Granny. I've just been moody lately."

"It's OK, B. Granny understands." She dug in her purse and handed me two quarters. "Get yourself some bubble gum. Maybe that will make you smile. After you finish shopping, maybe we can get a pretzel." She winked.

I guess I didn't hurt her feelings too bad. I let out a sigh and ran to the bubblegum machine in the middle of the mall and got one pink and one blue gumball. I gave the pink one to Mom, since it's her favorite. We waved to Granny Lily as we entered Victoria's Secret. Mom walked over to the PINK section, which I guessed was my area, and started picking out different styles without saying a word. Clearly, she was annoyed with my attitude.

"Come on to the fitting room."

I was glad to go, since the store was so crowded. Hopefully I wouldn't see anyone from school.

Before I could take off my shirt, Mom turned me around, holding my arm tight. "Blossom, I am sick of your attitude. I understand that you don't want to be here, but you don't have to treat your Granny Lily badly. She wanted to share this moment with us too."

My heart had that weak feeling, like when I see a sad story on YouTube about abused animals, or when I see Daddy in my dreams.

"I know, Mom. I apologized to her. I will try to control my attitude."

"I have a feeling something is going to happen soon."

We both knew what that something was, but we just sat there in silence. Then one of the fitting room attendants knocked on the door, interrupting our moment.

"Do you ladies need anything?"

Mom opened the door. I was glad my shirt was still on, because that would've been embarrassing. No one has seen my boobs except Granny Lily, Mom, and Suri.

"Yes. Can you measure her, please?"

I eyeballed the sizes Mom had picked out. Most of the bras were 32Bs.

The lady introduced herself as Jessica. Her thick, black-framed glasses were cool, similar to my Ray-Bans. Fortunately, I only have to wear them to see the board at school. My eyesight isn't that bad. Jessica's perfume was a little strong, which hurt my nose. I held my breath as she wrapped the measuring tape around my boobs. I was careful not to make eye contact. This moment was too awkward for small talk.

When Jessica was done calculating my measurements, she told us that I measured 32D. Because she spoke kind of loudly, everyone in the fitting area turned and stared. My face felt hot. I'd never felt so embarrassed. Mom looked stunned, but she asked Jessica to pick out a few more styles as we headed back into our fitting room. After closing the door, she turned to me with her eyes wide.

"We wear the same size. That explains the lack of support from your current bras."

Little did she know, I was starting to get used to having boobs. They made my shirts look better. I wouldn't dare tell Mom, though. She might cause a flood, and I really wanted to get home.

Jessica came back pretty fast, bringing lace, rainbow, super-padded, and multi- strapped bras. Mom handed the lace ones back, saying that I was too young for that style. Then we closed the door, and I tried on the rainbow-colored bra. It fit.

"Oh my God! These things are huge."

Mom giggled. She pulled out her phone and started texting vigorously. I'm sure she was telling everyone that I had huge boobs. The day was getting worse by the minute.

"Mom, can you not tell everyone? This is embarrassing."

"I'm not, honey. Granny Lily is texting me. She doesn't feel well. We have to go."

Excitement shot out of my fingers. I'd never gotten dressed so fast. I was so excited to get out of the fitting room. "So, we're not buying any of these?"

"No, Blossom. I'll come back tomorrow. In the meantime, you can wear one of my new bras at home."

"That's just weird. I'll wear my sports bra or something."

Jessica seemed a little disappointed that we were leaving without buying anything. Giggling to myself, I couldn't have been any happier. It didn't even bother me that we didn't have time to get a pretzel.

We met Granny Lily at the bench. Her pain must have been intense, because she closed her eyes as my mom helped her stand.

"I just need to put some cream on my knee, and I'll be fine."

"It's OK, Granny Lily. Can I help you put it on?"

"Of course, baby."

She hadn't called me baby in a long time. It felt good. I placed my hand in hers and we left the mall to find our SUV.

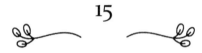

15

Having allergies for two days was miserable. The constant sneezing and itchy, watery eyes eventually turned into the stupid cough. My cough is like the sound a seal makes, but with more barking. My ability to change flowers with my fingertips is pretty cool, but I didn't think it would affect my allergies. I guess this means more pricking tests. The *Nova Book of Magic* has a remedy, but I've been too sick to even read it. Granny Lily was on her way over to help make soup, though.

"Aaaah-chooo!"

I pulled my light-purple baby blanket over my head, the one I used to pretend was a superhero cape. I wished I could run away from Anastasia so my neighbors wouldn't have to deal with my growing pains. For that matter, I wished I could run away from myself. Why couldn't I be like all the other little girls and grow up powerless? I'd rather be powerful like Oprah, Ellen DeGeneres, or Beyoncé. But no, I'm a Nova, and I have to have stupid superpowers.

Ever since this cough started back up, no animals have come to visit me. How could they trust me to heal them if I can't even heal myself? Rather than showing up at my treehouse, animals have been randomly running up to strangers. Considering that no one besides me can understand what they're saying, you can imagine how scary that is. There are so many news stories that I've stopped turning on the television. Mom says that people are staying indoors out of fear an animal will attack them. I wish I could help, but I can't even leave my room.

There are three weeks until the start of sixth grade, and I'm terrified. Hopefully Granny Lily's soup will make me better. I don't want to be known as the girl who barks like a seal. I'd rather be known for my powers, even though I'm not supposed to tell anyone about them. Unfortunately, my powers are the only things I can control right now.

I've heard that middle school is the hardest three years of a person's life. Kids are cruel, awkward, and trying to prove something to the world. Poppy said he used to get shoved into the lockers every day by the athletes until he became one himself. Mom used to cry every day before school because she was the quiet geek who had friends but was too shy to make new ones; Granny Lily said she was so skinny that the kids used to tease her by calling her Mosquito.

If the coolest people in my life had been bullied, then this eleven-year-old with pimples and newfound but uncontrollable superpowers was doomed. For my past two birthdays, I wished to be a normal kid, but my wishes continued to go unanswered.

That's it! What if I figured out a way to control my powers? If I could make them more than nature-related by transferring them to something more useful, then maybe people wouldn't treat me like a sideshow act.

Since the Novas are the only people I know with superpowers, I relied heavily on the internet for learning about magic. YouTube is filled with millions of magic tricks that turn out to be duds. With every failure, I grew more frustrated. Not knowing what else to do, I finally closed my laptop and went outside to my treehouse for some fresh air. The treehouse has become the one place where I feel like a normal kid. Mom finally got rid of most of my toys over the summer.

In my treehouse, I poured myself some imaginary tea, laid down on my faux fur rug, and sobbed. Through my tears I said, "I wish life was normal like before my dad died. I wish I could control these stupid powers. I know that I have to grow up, but why does it have to happen now?"

There was a shuffling noise near my bookshelf.

I stopped crying, wiped my tears away with the back of my hand, and stood up. I didn't hear the noise again.

Great! Not only do I have superpowers, now I'm hearing things. Maybe my next power will be a diagnosis? All of this is making me crazy!

The shuffling noise started again. I walked over to the bookshelf, and a book dropped out. I didn't remember putting it there. It was heavy, but beautiful and very old, bound in leather with silver and gold sparkles all over the cover. It kind of resembled the way I decorated my science spiral notebook yesterday. Except mine had black sparkles and quotes written all over it.

I traced a trembling finger over the letters on the cover:

NOVA FAMILY TREE: The Book of Mag Vol. 2.

The Book of Mag? Maybe the letters had fallen off? Mom never mentioned another book. Maybe she forgot.

Lately, my and Blossom's relationship has been more like the War of the Roses than the Gilmore Girls. Unfortunately, we both knew what to expect. Now eleven, Blossom is a powerhouse of raging hormones. Mom and I went through the same thing, but it was so many years ago that I can't remember when our relationship changed.

Her pediatrician predicted when she was nine that she would start her ruby within a year, and again when she turned ten. It still hasn't happened, but I suspect that with her new attitude, growth spurt, and mood swings, we're closer than ever.

I know Blossom's bad attitude is a strong indicator of pre-menstruation, but I still don't feel prepared for it. I've stowed away pads and panty liners. I've even put her old underwear in a different drawer, so she'll have "period panties" for the heavy days.

It tickles me to know that at such a young age, Blossom's boobs are already bigger than mine—well, at least before my augmentation. I got cosmetic surgery because I needed to feel whole again. Blossom even accompanied me to the appointment. I was glad we could share that moment. I don't want her to ever feel ashamed of her changing body, but to love herself and understand that sometimes people make changes to themselves not because they need to, but because they want to.

Sparks from the lone sparkler candle fell onto my large chocolate chip cookie cake. Since I was with Mom, Granny Lily, and Poppy, I inhaled and exhaled. And I touched the end of one of my curls, which begin to form a skinny braid all by itself and waved slowly over the flame until it went out and *poof!* I was another year older. After making a wish, I opened my eyes.

Granny Lily, Poppy, and Mom were all gone. Just Daddy was sitting in front of me, smiling.

"Daddy! What are you doing here?" I stood to give him a hug.

"Hey, Blossom. Considering that we only meet in one place, can't you answer that? You're asleep."

I guess that made sense. I did just have a birthday party.

"I never had a chance to celebrate a birthday with you, so I thought we could have our own celebration here. Turn around."

I turned and saw that on the window seat, there were eleven different treats. Cookies, candy, and my favorite, double-fudge ice cream. A single multi-color sparkling candle burned above them all. I couldn't help but smile, and my cheeks got wet.

"Who would have thought that ice cream would make Daddy's baby cry?" Daddy hugged me.

I wasn't crying because of the cake. I was crying because I hadn't realized how much I missed seeing him on my birthdays, holidays—life in general. Our nightly dream visits were great, but we'd missed out on seven years before those started. I squeezed him tighter, inhaling the sweet smell of his skin and looking at him longer than normal. I didn't want to ever forget him. We didn't know when or if these dreams would ever stop.

"I'm not sure how long candles burn in the dream realm, so you might want to blow them out." Daddy wiped his tears in a hurry, not wanting me to see him unhappy.

I remembered Mom saying that she'd just seen Daddy cry three times—on their wedding day, at my birth, and on the day he died. Inhaling slowly, filling my lungs with all the air in the room, I counted to eleven and then blew out the candles one by one, making the same wish each time.

"I don't have a gift for you tonight. Maybe I can help you eat all those treats?"

"It's OK. I was hoping you didn't have anything."

When the smoke from the last candle disappeared, I turned toward Daddy. He wasn't far behind me. Holding out my fingers like I do when using my powers, I placed my hand over his heart. My entire hand glowed gold. The intensity of Daddy's heartbeat grew stronger. I placed my ear on his chest and cried until the sun warmed my face and he was gone.

16

I sat in the backseat of our new red Mercedes G Wagon SUV in silence. This truck had to grow on me. I thought it was ugly the first time we test drove it. Mom thought she should reward herself for selling ten gowns in one day by buying her dream car. She'd been saving for years. I don't know if people shopped at Mom's store because they like her designs or to see if she would slip up and showcase the powers that the town whispered she had.

I was reading my favorite book series, *Diary of a Wimpy Kid*. The story of Greg going away to camp reminded of something that hadn't come up in a while, and I closed the book.

"I guess I am the last one of my friends."

Mom looked in the rearview mirror like she always did when talked in the car. I can't wait until I turn twelve, so she'll let me sit in the front the way Poppy, Granny Lily, and Suri let me. I'm not a baby, and I'll probably be this height for the rest of my life.

Mom says that sometimes when she stares at me, she sees herself staring back. It's kind of eerie how much we resemble one another.

"You're the last one of your friends to what?"

"Emma started her period two days ago, and she seems pretty sad. All my friends have officially gotten their rubies, Mom."

I felt defeated. Although my mom and the video we watched in class had prepared me for this moment, I still wasn't ready. Would I have to stop playing with my dolls? Or would I wake up the day after my first ruby and be an adult? This was all too much.

"I don't want to start. I'm scared. My childhood will be over all because of some stupid woman named Mother Nature. Stupid Eve! Why did she have to give Adam that apple? Why can't boys have these problems? Why do I have to have these stupid powers?"

My face became wet and hot. I'm pretty sure my eye color changed too, but I was too upset to look in the mirror.

"I don't want to grow up. I hope—hope I don't ever get my period—ruby—or whatever that stupid thing is called!"

With some compassion and relief in her voice, Mom said "Honey, it's going to happen. It's something we can't control. But you'll learn to accept and embrace it. That's life, my love."

"Who are you kidding, Mom? We both know that for me, life as I know it has changed forever. I already have four powers when I should only have one, and I'm frightened of what my period will bring."

"I would be afraid too, B. I am afraid. But I was afraid for myself, and it gets easier. I got one power after going through puberty. You're special. With every change, you've gained another power. That's a first. But you're a Nova, and you will get through this."

"It's pretty cool that I have powers, but I only just figured out how to control them. I would give them all up just to stay a kid forever."

"You will always be my baby."

"I know that, but I'm almost as tall as you, and we wear the same shoe size, and my boo—boo—my boobs are huge and embarrassing." I could barely say *boobs* through my uncontrollable sobs. "I wonder if I can use my powers to stop this nonsense."

Mom pulled over and shut off the engine. I could tell that she too couldn't take it any longer. All my changes had begun to affect her, or at least that's what I overheard her telling Granny Lily. Being able to control the rain was scary enough. Mom wasn't able to control her powers until she went to high school, and that was because she wasn't an emotional person, but she also told me that something about her teen years made her more sensitive. I am guessing puberty.

Raindrops started pattering against the windows. Without seeing my mom's face, I knew she was crying.

"Mom, don't cry."

Water drops of every size started to hit the windshield one by one. The longer Mom sat, the harder the drops fell.

I hopped into the front seat to give my mom a hug, wiping her tears away as I often have, especially after Daddy died. I didn't care if Anastasia flooded. We both needed to release our pent-up emotions.

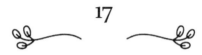

17

Sixth grade is finally here. I could barely sleep last night, I was so excited and nervous, so my dream with Daddy was a little spotty. I'm not sure I could even piece it together enough to tell Mom.

It was reassuring to know that Em and Jade would be meeting me in the lunchroom on Doomsday—that is, the first day of school. It shouldn't be so bad since most of us have been going to school together since kindergarten. Still, it was intimidating to think that we'd be roaming around with kids who were much bigger and almost in high school. During orientation last week, we were all given tours by assigned seventh-grade buddies. I've never had to leave class every hour, so I'm not sure how I'll make it to six classes in four minutes. Some are upstairs, and the gym is on the other side of the school. If my sense of direction is anything like my mom's, I'll never make it to class.

I think Mom was more anxious about me starting sixth grade than I was. We spent yesterday going over what to do in an emergency, what types of people to avoid, reputation, and maintaining straight As. Oh, the pressure!

I spent a lot of time last night unpacking and repacking my backpack, making sure that I didn't forget anything for the first day. While I was on summer vacation with my grandparents, my mom bought me a special backpack with a glittery "A" that matched my golden curls. I've decided to wear my hair curly this year, since Mrs. Joy always seemed nervous doing my hair. I can control its powers now, but I wouldn't want an accident to reveal my family's secret. Besides, I feel more grown-up not depending on Mom to comb my hair every morning.

Mom had picked out a grey button-up shirt with white stars and dark-blue skinny jeans for my first day of school. My brand-new white Converses, still in the box, were strategically placed on the floor under my jeans. It was sort of our tradition. I had so many cool new clothes. If only I could sleep in them. But I didn't want to get in trouble or wrinkle my shirt.

I couldn't wait to get dressed. The clock on my nightstand read 6:15 a.m., which meant I had 45 minutes until my alarm went off. This would be the first school year that Mom didn't have to wake me up. I was getting older, so she said I had to practice getting up by myself. I'm definitely not a morning person, though. We'd see how long this lasted before Mom had to start waking me up again. Maybe I could get a few more minutes of sleep to share my excitement with my dad—daddy.

I entered the place where I see my dad. It didn't take long. I guess the sleep deprivation from last night had gotten to me. Daddy was sitting on the end of my bed when I opened my eyes.

"Hey, sleepyhead, I thought you'd never make it. Pulled an all-nighter, huh?"

"Hi, Daddy! I'm so nervous about starting sixth grade."

"B, you'll be fine. I hate that I can't drive you to school myself, or even walk you to the door." He cleared his throat. I could tell he was getting emotional, so I got out of bed and walked over to give him a hug.

"It's OK, Daddy. I'll be sure to go to bed early tonight so I can tell you all about my first day of middle school. Maybe you can tell me what your first day was like, back in the day."

"Deal!"

We both laughed.

"Now, we only have a little time before your alarm goes off, and I have something to give you." Daddy walked over to my closet, knelt down by my hamper, and pulled out the most beautiful bouquet of red roses.

"Are those for Mom?"

"No, baby. These are for you."

I grabbed the bouquet and inhaled its sweetness. Each fold of the flowers was beautifully crafted. Daddy must've gotten these from God himself. I counted the roses. There were exactly eleven.

"Daddy, I thought a bouquet had twelve flowers. Did you forget one?"

He flashed a perfect smile, showing those twenty-six chiseled teeth. Then he took his left hand from behind his back, revealing a beautiful cherry blossom branch.

"This is for your Mom."

I didn't bother to ask, because I knew the bouquet, he had handed me was a clue to my next power. But what could a bouquet even mean? My body hadn't changed anymore. Oh no! What if this meant that I was starting my period?

"Daddy, am I getting another power? I hope these don't mean I'm starting my period. What if I start on the first day of school?"

I was asking too many questions without giving him time to answer. He kissed me on the forehead and said, "I actually don't know this time, Blossom." I could tell he was being sincere.

"Let's hope they're just a gift for starting middle school."

"It's possible. I'll see you tonight, B. I hope you have a great first day."

An annoying fire engine siren filled my ears, and the backs of my eyelids turned orange. The smell of pancakes and sausage drifted into my nose. Mom must not have been able to sleep either, because she almost never cooks breakfast.

I had just poured syrup on Blossom's first-day-of-school pancakes when I heard the rubber soles of her new Converses squeaking across the hardwood floor.

"Good morning, sixth-grader! Did you sleep well?"

"Not at all, but I did see Daddy, and he gave me these."

Before I could respond, Blossom pulled a beautiful bouquet of roses from behind her back.

"Those are beautiful, B. Daddy must've wanted to give you a gift for your first day."

"He wasn't sure what the roses are for, but he wanted me to give you this!" She pulled a cherry branch in full blossom from behind her back.

"For me?"

When I inhaled the sweet scent of the branch, my heart felt full like it did when he was alive. I knelt to take two vases from under the sink and took Blossom's bouquet to set it in water.

Blossom was already eating her pancakes. Mouth still full, she said, "I hope those flowers don't mean a new power. That could ruin my first day of school, not knowing what it would be or how to control it."

"I'm not sure, B, but considering that you brought something back for me, maybe Daddy just wanted to give you something to let you know that he's still here, even if he can't be physically."

"Maybe," Blossom said as she gulped down the last of her orange juice.

As I carefully placed the eleven roses in the vase, I saw something red fall into the water. "Blossom come here. Something was in the roses."

"Is it a bug?"

"I don't think so." I stuck my hand in the vase and picked it up. After, wiping the water off on my jeans, I opened my hand. On my palm lay a red stone.

"What is it, Mom?"

I lifted the stone between my thumb and index finger to get a better look. My eyes bulged with shock and my voice cracked. All I could do was whisper the word "ruby."

"Oh no! Not on my first day."

18

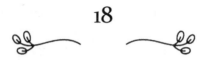

This was my first time having a locker with a combination lock. I practiced using the lock over and over with Mom. Right-left-right was harder than I thought. If I could just use the strength of my hair to open the lock. But there would be too many girls in the locker room, and my secret would be out. Luckily my combination is easy to remember: 01-03-33. I'm only afraid of having a brain fart and forgetting it. I don't want to be the only girl who can't change into her gym clothes because the nerves of being in a new school with older kids got the best of me.

Fortunately, my gym class wouldn't require proper dress until next week. The coach understood our anxiety. The stress of learning a new environment and finding our classes every period was enough.

The first day flew by. We didn't learn much, just spent every class introducing ourselves. I don't know why that was necessary. We all knew one another. Even though a lot of new people had moved to Anastasia, it didn't take long before everyone knew your business without even meeting you. There are a lot of gossips in town, including Granny Lily.

I met Mom at the flagpole, where we'd agreed to meet after school every day. It's gotten hard for Poppy to walk, so Mom has to pick me up now.

"Hey, B, how was your first day?"

"You just spend the passing period pushing through the eighth-graders. Since we're much smaller than them, I guess they don't see us. I wish I could use my hair to push them out of the way!"

"Aww, B, please try to remain calm. We have to keep our secret safe."

"I would drop out of school if I got detention."

"Why? Who said anything about detention?" Mom asked, trying to conceal her laughter.

"The principal told us that we'd get detention for horseplay, pushing in the hallways, being disrespectful, everything. I would drop out because it goes on your permanent record. When you try to get a job, you'll have 50 million detentions on your record!"

Mom couldn't take it any longer and burst into laughter. She said she couldn't believe what was coming out of my mouth.

"Teachers don't care about us. They just want our lunch money."

"That's not true, B."

"I know, Mom, but those eighth-graders are just rude. The seventh graders aren't as bad. Overall, everyone is so nice, and I'm so pretty."

"Oh, Blossom. Let's speak in complete sentences. Confident much?" she asked, winking. "I didn't get a call from the nurse today, so I am guessing you didn't start?"

"Start what?"

"Did you forget about the ruby that fell out of your bouquet?"

I guess all the craziness of the day had made me forget. "No, Mom, I haven't started. Maybe it was just a gift. I'm going to ask Poppy to drill a hole in the ruby, so I can make it into a necklace."

"Good idea, B. We have to stop by my store before we go home. I just got some new accessories. Maybe you can use one of the chains for your necklace."

"I hope Daddy can bring me—us more gifts."

"I hope so." Mom smiled.

When we got home, I dropped my new, very heavy backpack by the front door and ran up to my room to change into some old clothes before going out to my treehouse. Poppy and Granny Lily were coming over later for dinner, and I couldn't wait to tell them about my dream, my gifts from Daddy, and my first day in sixth grade.

I slipped off my pants and unbuttoned my grey shirt, throwing both into the hamper in my closet. I suddenly realized that I hadn't used the restroom all day because I was afraid of being late for class, and I had to pee so badly that I barely made it to the toilet.

Pulling down my underwear, I sat down on the cold toilet and looked down at my green polished toes. Then I noticed something in my underwear.

Without wiping, I pulled my underwear to my knees and headed straight for the stairs.

"Mom! Look!"

Mom was taking out the ingredients for dinner and glanced around the pantry door to see what was going on. When she saw the quarter-sized drop of blood in my panties, her eyes went big and her mouth dropped to the floor.

"Oh my God, you started!"

I could tell from her confused expression that Mom was trying to gather her thoughts. She took two small steps toward me, but her brain must not have communicated with her body, because she fainted.

"Are you OK, Mom?"

My panties were still around my knees. I couldn't move. I guess that's what being in shock feels like.

Pushing herself back against the pantry door, Mom put her face in her hands and began to weep. I guess they were happy tears because a storm did not start.

Finally, gathering herself to stand, she walked over to me. She helped me pull my panties up, and we hugged. Then she whispered the four words that I wasn't ready to hear: "You started your ruby."

The tighter we hugged, the faster the tears rolled down our cheeks. Droplets of rain started to hit the windows again.

"Mom, why are you crying?"

"Oh, baby, you're growing up. I knew this was going to happen at some point. I just wasn't ready."

"Does this mean I have to stop playing with my toys?"

"You can play with them forever if you'd like. It doesn't mean anything you're doing now has to stop. You'll be Mommy's little girl forever." She kissed me on the forehead. Then she stepped back, pinching her arms so that her tears and the rain would stop.

"Go get in the shower, baby. I'll show you how to put on a pad, when you get out." She handed me one she had purchased earlier from the bag on the counter. "I love you."

"I love you too, Mom—forever and always. But Mom, you have to stop crying or it's going to flood, and I won't be able to go to school tomorrow."

"You're right," she chuckled as she wiped the last tears from her eyelashes.

While showering, I watched the streams of womanhood trail down my legs. I couldn't tell if I was crying or if the water was splashing on my face. As hard as the news was for Mom, it was hard for me to absorb too. From this day forward, my life would be forever different. At eleven years old, I had not only crossed the puberty line, I would probably gain another superpower.

Having the pad on felt weird, and it gave me a fluttering feeling in my stomach, like butterflies were crashing into one another inside me.

"Mom, can I sleep with you tonight?"

"Of course. That will make it easier for me to keep an eye on the flow of your period."

"Mom!"

"What, B?"

"Talking about my period just sounds weird. Can we just call it a ruby?"

I must have smiled, because Mom stuck her index finger in the little crescent on my cheek.

"How could I forget? Yes, we can just refer to it as your ruby."

"Maybe there's a page in the *Nova Book of Magic* about using my power to make these boobs go away. Or at least shrink a little."

Mom laughed. "I forgot to tell you that your breasts will get bigger every month around the time of your ruby. They may be a little sensitive too. That's how you'll know it's going to start."

"You mean my boobs are going to get even bigger than this?"

"They're swollen, now Blossom. That's probably as big as they'll get, and then they'll shrink back to their normal size."

"Phew!"

"Finish getting dressed so I can tell you more about caring for yourself during your ruby."

"OK, Mom. By the way, I don't want to eat ice cream. I have the strange urge to eat a bunch of chocolate."

"That's nothing new, Blossom." Mom walked away laughing.

I headed to toward my bedroom as Mom walked into the living room. I could hear the silence of our feet as we both paused but didn't turn around. I didn't have a power to see what was going on behind me, but I saw Mom's reflection in the mirror by the couch. I think we both knew there was a change, but we both kept it to ourselves.

Rather than turning on my laptop or looking at my phone when I got to my room, I opened my closet to enter my treehouse. Still in my towel, I dumped out the brown woven toy basket that had started collecting dust in the corner and proceeded to play. It was the last basket of toys that I hadn't yet donated to the Salvation Army. I wasn't going to let a little ruby stop me from being a kid. Playing with toys might be my last way to hold onto my childhood a little longer.

I repeated the words that Poppy said to me before dropping me off at my mom's dress store last week: "Promise me that you'll stay a little girl as long as you can."

I promised.

As my Littlest Pet Shop was ending its last pretend lecture of the day, the *Nova Book of Magic* fell off the shelf and landed open. This had better be a good power, I thought to myself. I don't want to be a complete freakshow my first week of school.

As I turned to the book, ready to meet my fate, I found that the page—page 23—was blank. Flipping back, I saw that the five preceding pages were also blank. What did this mean? Was I losing my powers?

Then, as I traced my fingers over one of the blank pages, words started to appear. After a minute, the page read

> For you formed my inward parts; you covered me in my mother's womb . . . I am fearfully and wonderfully made. —Psalms 139:13-14

I assumed this was a quotation from the Bible. I needed to call Poppy. He was the only person I knew who had read the entire book.

19

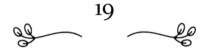

First period was boring as usual. I never participated much in theatre. I spent most of the 45 minutes, staring out the window. Sibley Park was faint in the distance. All I could think of was running through the grass, letting the wind batter my face as I raced to climb the flimsy branches. I just wanted to run away and hide. Why did we have to refer to classes as periods? Well, at least when it was that time of the month. It was like the universe had something against school-age girls.

Mrs. Q tapped me on the shoulder and asked if I was OK. I nodded, but my face became wet. She knelt down next to my desk, but I hid my face from the class. The bell rang, but Mrs. Q held my wrist and whispered, "Go to the restroom. I'll let Mr. Peak know that you'll be late." She gently squeezed my wrist and smiled. "We all have bad days. Take care of yourself."

"Thank you." I wiped my face with the sleeve of my purple hoodie and headed to the restroom.

Placing several layers of toilet paper over the seat, I made a makeshift sanitary throne to cry on, being sure to muffle myself with my hands. Every time I closed my eyes, I could see the brown dog with white spots exhale for the last time. Mr. Little cried so hard his cane fell over.

After several minutes, I pulled myself together. I blew my nose with the hard toilet paper. Wiping my eyes with it was even worse. It felt like sandpaper scraping my face. As I stood up to unlock the stall, I felt a rush of liquid escape my body and drip onto my underwear.

"Oh no! Can this day get any worse?"

Luckily, I had an emergency purse in my backpack. Suri gave it to me for Christmas last year. One side was black leather and other a mixture of blue, red, white, and green sequins. Inside it I had packed a pair of panties and four pads. Mom said I should have enough pads and panty liners to change every two to four hours. Hygiene is very important for girls on and off their rubies.

I quickly pulled off my pants and changed into clean underwear, throwing the ruby-stained panties into the small trashcan on the wall of the stall. I was careful not to make a lot of noise while opening the pad. I also didn't want to drop it on the floor like I did when I was practicing. Placing the thick cloth into the little white path of my underwear in one swoop, I pulled up my pants, then I washed my hands and headed to my second period—class. How fitting, I laughed to myself.

Mr. Peak smiled when I entered. Looking at the clock, I realized that I had been in the bathroom for thirty minutes. Hopefully, I didn't miss anything too important.

I felt a little better at lunch, especially after apologizing to Emma for being so grumpy earlier. Jade bought me two brownies. She could tell Mother Nature was not my friend today. I guess it's a girl thing.

Sixth period was science, pretty much my favorite class. Today, Mr. Weinstein, who prefers us to call him Einstein, showed us how to make flowers change color. For a second, I thought he was going to tell the class that he had magical powers, but then I saw six tubes of food coloring at each station. Poppy showed me this trick when I was four years old. But even though I can change a flower with my power, science stuff always makes me giddy.

"Blossom, do you want to be my Vanna White?"

"Sure, I guess. I'm not sure who Vanna White is, though."

My classmates laughed, and Mr. Weinstein blushed. Even the bald spot on his head turned red.

"I can't be that old. *Wheel of Fortune* still comes on, right?"

"Oh, yeah, my mom watches that show sometimes."

Mr. Weinstein placed four glass beakers on his desk and filled them with water. "OK, Blossom, add a different color to each beaker."

I carefully poured twenty drops of color each into three glasses, and the water quickly changed into my favorite colors: blue, purple, and green.

"Now the hard part. I want you to place each of these white daisies in a beaker." As he put the daisies in my hand, I almost forgot about my flower-changing power. I held my breath, my heart nearly beating out of my chest as I walked over to the beakers. I held my index fingers out from my hands, making sure that they didn't touch the stems.

"Are you planning on shooting me with you finger?" Mr. Weinstein joked.

"No." My face felt warm. "I think I might be allergic to this kind of flower."

I played dumb. I know the names of every flower, and I'm not allergic to any of them, but no one else knew that. Mr. Weinstein turned red again. He held out his hand and said that he would take over from there.

He put the flowers into the beakers. As he turned to tell the class that we would see their colors change before the bell, his lab coat caught one of the daisies and tipped it over. I caught the beaker before it crashed to the ground. Just a droplet of blue water escaped.

"Great catch!"

As I set the beaker upright, the stem of the daisy brushed my finger. I held my breath. From the corner of my eye, I could see tiny gold sparkles dancing up the stem and onto the petals. I closed my eyes, hoping my classmates were paying attention to the teacher and not me.

"Cool!" someone yelled.

Mr. Weinstein turned to look where the kid was pointing. Not only was the daisy changing from white to blue, it was turning into scorpion grass.

Everyone's eyes were wide. Our teacher's mouth fell open. I could only pretend to be as shocked as everyone else.

"Impossible," Mr. Weinstein mumbled.

Ashley, who sat in the front row, glared at me. It was the same way she'd glared at me in fifth grade the day the raccoon talked to me. My heart dropped into my stomach. Then the bell sounded, and everyone started packing up in a hurry. Mr. Weinstein picked up the beaker holding the scorpion grass. His hands trembled nervously, and he dropped it to the floor. When the glass shattered, just a simple white daisy lay on the floor surrounded by blue water and glass.

The rest of the day went, fine apart from the few times I passed Sarah and Ashley in the hallway. They just stared at me and whispered in one another's ears. I texted Mom, but she didn't respond.

It was Poppy's turn to pick me up from school. It was also Fudge Friday, and the only thing I wanted to do was drown myself in hot fudge at my favorite ice cream shop at the pier. I didn't want to run into Mr. Little, though, so I asked Poppy to take me to Scoops by Mom's dress shop. The fudge isn't as great, but their chocolate sprinkles will do.

We sat outside. The back patio of Scoops opened onto the marina. The waves were steady, crashing into monochromatic blue bliss. The sun burned hot on my face. I'm pretty sure my cheeks were turning red. I pulled off my purple sweatshirt and put it on the seat next to my backpack. The sweet aroma of cherry blossoms entered my nose and came right back every time I exhaled.

Poppy came back with my chocolate fudge brownie with extra chocolate chip cookie crumbles. He still claims to hate chocolate, so he ate a banana split instead, with strawberry and caramel syrup.

"You were pretty quiet in the car. Is everything OK?"

"Poppy, I'm pretty sure you already saw."

"No Blossom, I—"

"Don't say that! You sniffed like you do when you're not telling the truth!"

"You got me, Blossom. You handled yourself well in science class."

"I did? But I just stood there. I think Ashley and Sarah know about my powers."

"How so?" Poppy removed his glasses. I guess he didn't see that part in his vision. I told him the story of the raccoon talking to me in the fifth grade, and about today when the flower changed.

He put his glasses back on and said he would take care of it. Poppy always wears his glasses when he doesn't want to have a vision.

I was losing my appetite, and my brownie dream was becoming a muddy disaster. After everything that happened today, I had almost forgot my ruby had started. I pulled my sequined purse out of my backpack and excused myself.

There were red circles lightly dusted on Poppy's cheeks. He seemed a little nervous, and cleared his throat. "Do you need me call your mom?"

"No, I'm fine. I'll be back in a sec."

Poppy stuck the white plastic spoon in the vanilla mound and shoved his glass dish away. He looked sad but said nothing. I think he's having a hard type accepting that I'm growing up and he can't do anything about it.

The cedar-planked stall was designed by Mr. Scoop, who thought it would be cool to use old wood from Mr. Little's fishery, one of the many hidden gems of Anastasia. Pretty much everything here comes from the locals.

A light tapping on the concrete floor interrupted my focus on the décor. It seemed to be getting closer. I remembered locking the door, though. Maybe I was going crazy?

I flushed the toilet, threw my old pad in the trash, opened the heavy stall door, and almost fell back after seeing Roger the squirrel standing on the floor by the sink.

"I didn't mean to scare you, but this is the only way I can speak to you."

"Go away!"

Roger tugged at my pant leg. "Blossom! I have good news!"

"What's so great about an animal dying that I was supposed to save?" I started washing my hands even more roughly with the soap. My face felt hot, but I didn't want to cry. There were no more tears left in my body.

"She woke up after you left. We didn't think it would be a good idea for her to just be magically healed while you were there. There are rumors around town about your family. So, I told Sally—oh, that's her name—I told her to play dead."

"What?" My face felt hot, not because I was sad but because I was angry. "Why didn't you just tell me that. I've been avoiding the pier for weeks?" I backed Roger into a corner.

"I tried, but you just yelled at me. I don't know how to write, so I couldn't leave you a note."

I dropped to my knees. For the first time all day, I felt relief.

There was a knock at the door. It was Poppy. "Are you OK in there? Mr. Scoop said he heard you talking and thought you might need help."

"Oh, I'm fine. I was just singing a song."

I lifted Roger up to the window and whispered in his ear to meet me at my treehouse tomorrow. I kissed him on the cheek, and he crawled onto the drainpipe outside. When I opened the door, Poppy and Mr. Scoop were standing there with an uneasy look on their faces.

"It's OK, guys, I was just handling girl business. The restroom's all yours."

Poppy thanked Mr. Scoop for checking on me. Mr. Scoop patted Poppy's shoulder and said he couldn't believe how much I'd grown. I knew that was code for "She's got her period. Good luck."

I grabbed Poppy by the hand. He squeezed my palm twice, letting me know that he knew what had really happened in the restroom.

"Let me get you to Rain's store before she calls a search party."

"Good idea, Poppy. Besides, I have so much to tell her."

"I'm sure you do, baby."

I walked Blossom back to her room. Her eyes already closed, she climbed into her bed exhausted. I didn't want her to miss seeing her dad in the dream realm. Maybe he had more information about what to expect next from our pubescent daughter.

The hallway light peeked through the half-open door, letting me see the golden-brown curls piled messily atop Blossom's head. It was midnight when I kissed her cheek, tracing every hair on the back of her neck with my finger. Ever since she was a baby, I've touched her hair to make sure she stayed asleep.

Before I left, I sat and watched my not-so-little girl sleep. I realized that Blossom was no longer my baby, but a young lady who will bloom forever, living up to her name.

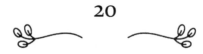

20

I opened one eye and realized that Mom had put me in my own bed. That was weird because I didn't have any dreams last night. Maybe I was still dreaming? The clock on my nightstand said 6:45 a.m. My alarm hadn't gone off. I sat up quickly.

There was a pounding noise coming from somewhere. It wasn't urgent or violent, but calm like a heartbeat. As I woke up more, it stayed in my ears. Could this be a new power? I didn't sleep in my bed last night, so I didn't get a chance to talk to Daddy. No wait, I was in my bed, but I didn't remember how or when I got here. He must have been upset since I promised to meet him. I pulled my pillow over my head to drown out the sound, hoping that would keep me from having to face another power or to face losing them all.

The noise still didn't stop. I started thinking about my daddy's death. Because he died when I was so young, I'd never sat and pondered what exactly killed him. How does your heart just stop beating?

With every moment, the heartbeat sound became more pronounced. Am I going crazy? Am I still dreaming? I can't be dreaming! Daddy would be here. I usually dream of Daddy every night, but last night—I can't remember.

"Oh no! Please God, don't take the one thing I had left of my Dad."

I started panicking, muffling my screams with my pillow. I didn't want to wake up Mom. She told me that emotions were a part of this change, but this was pretty intense. I put my hands over my ears and closed my eyes as tight as I could, hoping to hold on to the memories and dreams I had of my dad. Every sound was drowned out except the sound of a beating heart.

The longer I sat, the more I calmed down. Feeling a litter better, I finally opened my eyes slowly, realizing that I might have just had a bad dream.

My alarm clock was blaring. I must be going crazy; it was 6:50, the time I'd set it to go off. I needed the five extra minutes of sleep. I forgot that Mom had told me to set my alarm for 6:30, since I had to shower in the morning instead of at night. This stupid ruby was getting in the way of my sleep.

As I got up to head to Mom's room, I could still hear the knocking. Mom heard it too, because she met me in the hallway.

"Morning, Blossom. Are you feeling OK? Do you have cramps?"

"No. I had a weird dream, and then I heard knocking that wouldn't stop."

"Me too, but no one was there by the time I got downstairs. Maybe we had the same dream."

"Maybe." I shrugged.

"Go shower. I have a client who needs to have her dress fitted before the store opens, so Poppy will be here in a little while to take you to school.

"OK, Mom. You didn't tell him about my ruby, did you?"

"No."

"Good. I just promised him that I would stay a kid as long as I could. I don't want to disappoint him."

As I turned toward the bathroom, another knock came at the door. I paused, because it was too early for Poppy to pick me up, but I wasn't allowed to open the door to strangers. Maybe Poppy was here because he'd had a vision about Ashley and Sarah. Or maybe he wanted to tell me that I'm not his little girl anymore because of what happened at Scoops. My stomach tightened with fear.

Mom came out of her room, retying her silk grey robe.

"I'll get it, Mom. I think it's Poppy."

Mom walked down the stairs quickly behind me. We reached the front door at the same time. I could see the outline of a tall man through the frosted glass. I knew it was Poppy. I opened the door, even though I wasn't ready to see his sad face. I made eye contact with the tall man at the door.

"Good morning Pop—Daddy?"

CPSIA information can be obtained
at www.ICGtesting.com
Printed in the USA
BVHW091937041121
620791BV00016B/683

9 781736 889947